MADAM & EVE The Fourth Domestic REVOLUTION

By Stephen Francis & Rico

To our loving wives ... who often give us the headlines, the deadlines ... and sometimes even the punchlines

Published in 2019 in South Africa by Jacana Media
10 Orange Street, Auckland Park, 2092
PO Box 291784, Melville, 2109
www.jacana.co.za

ISBN 978-1-4314-2940-0
Job number 003618

Printed by **novus** print, a division of Novus Holdings

OTHER MADAM & EVE BOOKS

Madam & Eve Collection (Rapid Phase, 1993, reprint 1999)
Free At Last (Penguin Books, 1994)
All Aboard for the Gravy Train (Penguin Books, 1995)
Somewhere over the Rainbow Nation (Penguin Books, 1996)
Madam & Eve's Greatest Hits (Penguin Books, 1997)
Madams are from Mars, Maids are from Venus (Penguin Books, 1997)
It's a Jungle Out There (David Philip, 1998)
International Maid of Mystery (David Philip, 1999)
Has anyone seen my Vibrating Cellphone? (interactive.Africa, 2000)
The Madams are Restless (Rapid Phase, 2000)
Crouching Madam, Hidden Maid (Rapid Phase, 2001)
Madam & Eve, 10 Wonderful Years (Rapid Phase, 2002)
The Maidtrix (Rapid Phase, 2003)
Gin & Tonic for the Soul (Rapid Phase, 2004)
Desperate Housemaids (Rapid Phase, 2005)
Madams of the Caribbean (Rapid Phase, 2006)
Bring me my (new) Washing Machine (Rapid Phase, 2007)
Madam & Eve Unplugged (Rapid Phase, 2008)
Strike While The Iron Is Hot (Jacana, 2009)
Twilight of the Vuvuzelas (Jacana, 2010)

Mother Anderson's Secret Book of Wit & Wisdom (Jacana, 2011)
The Pothole at the End of the Rainbow (Jacana, 2011)
Twenty (Jacana, 2012)
Keep Calm and Take Another Tea Break (Jacana, 2013)
Send in the Clowns (Jacana, 2014)
Shed Happens (Jacana, 2015)
Take Me to Your Leader (Jacana, 2016)
Hadeda La Land (Jacana, 2017)
The Guptas Ate My Homework! (Jacana, 2018)
Jamen sort kaffe er pa mode nu, Madam! (Gyldendal, Denmark, 1995)
Jeg gyver Mandela Skylden for det her! (Gyldendal, Denmark, 1995)
Alt under kontrol I Sydafrika! (Bogfabrikken, Denmark, 1997)
Men alla dricker kaffet svart nufortiden, Madam! (Bokfabrikken, Sweden, 1998)
Madame & Eve, Enfin Libres! (Vents D'Ouest, France, 1997)
Votez Madame & Eve (Vents D'Ouest, France, 1997)
La coupe est pleine (Vents D'Ouest, France, 1998)
Rennue-Ménage à deux (Vents D'Ouest, France, 1999)
En voient de toutes les couleurs (Vents D'Ouest, France, 2000)
Madame vient de Mars, Eve de Venus (Vents D'Ouest, France, 2000)
Madam & Eve (LIKE, Finland, 2005)

MADAM & EVE APPEARS REGULARLY IN:
Daily Maverick, The Star, Saturday Star, Herald, Mercury, Witness, Daily Dispatch, Cape Times, Pretoria News, Diamond Fields Advertiser, Die Volksblad, EC Today, Kokstad Advertiser, The Botswana Advertiser, The Namibian.

TO CONTACT MADAM & EVE:
PO Box 413667, Craighall 2024, Johannesburg, South Africa
ricos@rico.co.za
www.madamandeve.co.za
Follow Madam & Eve on Facebook: www.facebook.com/madamandevecartoon
Follow Madam & Eve on Twitter @madamevecartoon

THE PRESENT: THREE WORKERS ON THE BACK OF A BAKKIE.

THE FUTURE: THREE WORKERS ON THE BACK OF A **SELF-DRIVING** BAKKIE.

ALRIGHT, CLASS. ENGLISH VOCABULARY QUIZ. YOU HAVE 30 MINUTES. ...BEGIN!

"QUESTION ONE: WHAT IS THE DEFINITION OF "ARTIFICIAL INTELLIGENCE"?

WRITING THE ANSWERS TO A SCHOOL QUIZ ON THE BACK OF YOUR HAND.

TIC TIC TIC TIC TIC TIC TIC TIC TIC TIC TIC TIC TIC TIC TIC TIC TIC TIC TIC

IS THERE **ANYBODY** IN THIS HOUSE **NOT** TEXTING, WHATSAPPING, SNAP-CHATTING, BLOGGING OR INSTAGRAMMING?!!

TIC TIC TIC TIC TIC TIC TIC TIC TIC TIC TIC

AH. DUSTING.

I GIVE UP.

TIC TIC TIC TIC TIC

TIC TIC TIC TIC

MADAM & Eve

BY STEPHEN FRANCIS & RICO

LOOK, MADAM! THERE'S NO DRIVER! MUST BE ONE OF THOSE SELF-DRIVING MINIBUS TAXIS I HEAR THEY'RE TESTING.

OH.

BUT CAN YOU IMAGINE WHAT IT WILL BE LIKE WHEN THERE'S SELF-DRIVING VEHICLES EVERYWHERE IN SOUTH AFRICA?

SELF-DRIVING BLUE LIGHT CONVOYS THAT ACTUALLY DRIVE SAFELY.

© RAPID PHASE - 2019

HIJACKERS AND HAWKERS WOULD BE COMPLETELY PUZZLED.

THERE WOULD BE AN AUTOMATIC "COOL DRINK DISPENSER" THAT POPS OUT AT ROADBLOCKS.

SPROING!

ALTHOUGH... IF THE SELF-DRIVING VEHICLE BREAKS DOWN, IT COULD BE IN BIG TROUBLE...

Help! Somebody help me!

LOOK-- THERE GOES A SELF-DRIVING VEHICLE NOW.

HOW CAN YOU BE SURE?

TWO REASONS: ONE-- THERE'S NO ONE BEHIND THE STEERING WHEEL. AND TWO ...

...THERE'S A BIG SIGN ON THE BACK.

HOW IS MY SELF-DRIVING? Call 088 888 5599

The
scent
of
greed.

The
lingering
aroma
of
corruption.

The
odour of a
blazing
New Dawn
economy.

RECESSION

A pungent new
fragrance from
eau de ANC.

RECESSION

*Just TRY
and
afford it!*

HI. YOU LOOK
GREAT TODAY!
CAN I **BORROW**
TWENTY BUCKS?
... HI! YOU LOOK
GREAT ...

HI!
YOU
LOOK--

...AND WE'RE BACK
WITH MORE ON THE
RECESSION
THAT WILL AFFECT
EVERYONE ...

@#☆@)!

... I LOOK **WHAT?**

ER...
NEVER
MIND.

WELL?
HOW'D
IT GO?

≡SIGH≡
... **TIMING**
IS
EVERYTHING.

BUT **THIS**
TIME, I CAN
PROVE THE
DOG ATE MY
HOMEWORK.

CHECK IT OUT.
VIDEO
FOOTAGE
OF THE
NEIGHBOUR'S
DOG ENTERING
THE **KITCHEN**.

WOOF!
WOOF!

WHY IS YOUR
HOMEWORK
SITTING IN
THE **DOG'S**
BOWL?

OOPS.
WRONG
CLIP.
GIVE
ME A
SECOND.

MADAM & Eve

BY STEPHEN FRANCIS & RICO

RAMAPHORIA

Noun: the short-lived feeling of hope and euphoria when Cyril Ramaphosa was appointed president.

BUT WHY **STOP** THERE?

THERE'S **MORE**...

RAMNESIA

Noun: not remembering all the bad decisions Cyril Ramaphosa made in the past.

I FORGET...DID CYRIL RAMAPHOSA **KNOW** ABOUT STATE CAPTURE, OR NOT?

RAMBIGUOUS

Adjective: how Cyril plans to bail out SAA and the SABC is anyone's guess.

SOUTH AFRICAN

RAMARANDS

Noun: our battered currency... now worth even less.

RAMBIDEXTROUS

Adjective: supporting Cyril but still voting for other political parties at the same time.

EFF

DA

RAMASELFIE

Noun: bumping into Cyril out walking and taking a picture with the president.

Click.

RAMBUSH

Noun: a sudden and unexpected attack on Cyril by opposition parties in parliament.

POINT OF ORDER!

RAMAPATHY

Noun: when you've stopped caring and just don't give a @#%$ about politics anymore.

RAMAPHOBIA

Noun: what the DA and EFF suffer from.

DA

RAMALAMADINGDONG

Noun: anyone who believes the president's economic stimulus package will actually work.

©RAPID PHASE·2018

COMING UP... THE FIRST EVER LIVE **REMOTE STATE CAPTURE TESTIMONY** FROM AN UNDISCLOSED **SECRET** SAFE HOUSE LOCATION IN DUBAI.

...THE **GUPTAS** ARE STANDING BY TO GIVE THEIR SIDE OF THE STORY...

...AND WE'LL BE RIGHT BACK AFTER **THIS!**

HUH?

WHEN YOU ABSOLUTELY NEED TO GET AWAY-- FLY **EMIRATES!**

THEY'RE SELLING **ADVERTISING?!**

SO, **DUDUZANE**... YOU'VE AGREED TO TESTIFY ABOUT **STATE CAPTURE.**

ABSOLUTELY. I WANT MY **DAY** IN **COURT.**

...JUST LIKE MY **FATHER.**

...BUT YOUR **FATHER** HAS BEEN **AVOIDING** HIS "DAY IN COURT" FOR OVER A **DECADE.**

EXACTLY.

THAT'S THE KIND OF "DAY IN COURT" I CAN **LIVE** WITH.

MADAM & Eve

BY STEPHEN FRANCIS & RICO

POSSIBLY SOME TIME IN THE NEAR FUTURE...

YOU KNOW, POP... I REALLY **ENJOY** THESE **DINNERS** WE SPEND TOGETHER. JUST **YOU** ... **ME** ...

... AND **200** OTHER GUYS IN ORANGE JUMPSUITS.

OH, CHEER UP, DAD. IT'S FRIDAY-- "FISHFINGER NIGHT."

EISH, DUDUZANE. **TRUMP** HAD THE RIGHT **IDEA**! HE **PARDONED** EVERYBODY! WHAT WAS I **THINKING**? WHY DIDN'T I PARDON **MYSELF**?

YEAH! AND PARDON **ME** ALSO!... **RIGHT**, DAD?

HUH? ER ... YEAH. PARDON **YOU** ALSO.

YO -- "MISTER PRESIDENT." YOU GONNA **EAT** THAT **DESSERT**?

GO AHEAD AND TAKE IT, BUBBA.

SHH. HOW MUCH **MONEY** DID YOU PUT AWAY **OFFSHORE** IN **DUBAI**, DUDUZANE?

ME? HOW MUCH DID **YOU** PUT AWAY?

I ASKED **YOU** FIRST.

OKAY. WE'LL SAY IT **TOGETHER**. READY? ONE ... TWO ... **THREE**!

@RAPID PHASE- 2018

I GUESS WE HAVE SOME **TRUST** ISSUES TO WORK THROUGH, DAD.

WELL ... WE HAVE **ELEVENTY** YEARS TOGETHER.

ELEVENTY?!

DAMMIT, YOU KNOW I'M NO GOOD WITH **MATHS**!

RELAX. WE CAN WATCH SOME TV.

WHAT'S ON?

LET'S SEE... "THE SHAWSHANK REDEMPTION", "ESCAPE FROM ALCATRAZ" ... "PRISON BREAK" ...

GROAN!

AND IN INTERNATIONAL NEWS... ONE OF THE MOST DANGEROUS WEATHER SYSTEMS EVER-- HURRICANE FLORENCE, IS ABOUT HIT THE UNITED STATES.

WHAT'S **WORSE** THAN HURRICANE **FLORENCE?**

...WHAT?

HURRICANE **EDITH!** GET IT?! HURRICANE **EDITH!!** HAHAHA! HEE HEE HEE!

...LOOKS LIKE RAIN.

THANDI! IS THAT CHEWING **GUM?!**

ER... YES, MISS.

FINE. THEN BRING THE PACKET UP HERE SO YOU CAN **SHARE** IT WITH THE **REST** OF THE CLASS.

SLAM!

HOW WAS SCHOOL?

LOUSY.

...MY **GUM** GOT EXPROPRIATED.

THANDI! ARE YOU CHEWING **GUM** AGAIN?!

WHO, **ME?** ABSOLUTELY NOT, MISS!

FINE! WELL, WHATEVER IT IS, BRING THE WHOLE PACKET UP HERE, SO WE CAN **SHARE** IT WITH THE WHOLE **CLASS!**

SLAM! I HATE SCHOOL!!

NOW WHAT?

YESTERDAY, THEY **EXPROPRIATED** MY CHEWING **GUM.** TODAY THEY **NATIONALISED** MY **GUMMY BEARS!**

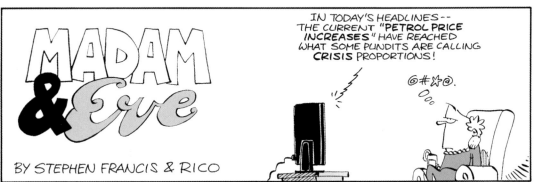

MADAM & Eve

BY STEPHEN FRANCIS & RICO

IN TODAY'S HEADLINES-- THE CURRENT "PETROL PRICE INCREASES" HAVE REACHED WHAT SOME PUNDITS ARE CALLING **CRISIS** PROPORTIONS!

@#*@.

UBERING TO THE BOTTLE STORE'S GOING TO COST A FORTUNE NOW.

YES!

WOO HOO!!

ODD. GOGO DOESN'T USUALLY GET SO EXCITED.

I'M **RICH!!**

RICH, I TELL YOU!

I FOUND A FULL TWENTY LITRE CAN OF PETROL IN THE GARAGE!

I'M RICH!

GROWN-UPS. THEY'RE ALWAYS SO SARCASTIC.

WHO'S BEING **SARCASTIC?!**

Row 1

QUICK QUESTION: WHAT'S "PETROLEUM JELLY"?

IT'S VASELINE, ISN'T IT?

"PETROLEUM JELLY?" THAT'S WHAT YOU **TURN** INTO AT THE **PETROL STATION** WHEN YOU SEE HOW MUCH THE PRICE HAS GONE UP!

GET IT ?! PETROLEUM JELLY!! HEE HEE HEE!! HOO HOO !!

MAYBE ONE DAY WHEN I DRIVE A CAR, I WON'T FIND IT FUNNY EITHER.

Row 2

RECENT OPINION POLLS SHOW THE PRESIDENT'S POPULARITY CLIMBING-- PUNDITS ARE CALLING IT A STATE OF "**RAMAPHORIA**."

WHAT'S "RAMAPHORIA"?

WHEN PEOPLE ARE **OPTIMISTIC** ABOUT PRESIDENT RAMAPHOSA'S **GOOD** CHOICES SO FAR.

WHAT ABOUT HIS "**NOT-SO-GOOD CHOICES**"? DO PEOPLE **FORGET** ABOUT THOSE?

SOME-TIMES...

...IT'S CALLED "RAMNESIA."

MOM!

Row 3

RAMAPHORIA

Noun: the short-lived feeling of hope and optimism when Cyril Ramaphosa was appointed president.

WAIT-- THERE'S **MORE!**

RAMANOMICS

Noun: accepting those huge Chinese "no strings attached" loans.

RAMAGEDDON

Noun: what some fear will happen if land reform isn't handled properly.

RAMASKEPTIC

Noun: someone who's not convinced by the president's economic stimulus package.

HMPH.

EVE-- HOW DO YOU **TEXT** SO **QUICKLY**... AND USING ONLY **ONE HAND**?!!

I DUNNO. LOTS OF **PRACTISE**, I GUESS.

TIC TIC TIC TIC TIC TIC TIC TIC TIC TIC TIC

TIC TIC TIC TIC TIC TIC TIC TIC TIC TIC TIC TIC TIC

VRRRR!!

TIC TIC TIC TIC TIC TIC TIC TIC TIC TIC TIC TIC TIC TIC TIC

TIC TIC TIC TIC TIC TIC TIC TIC TIC TIC TIC TIC TIC TIC

I'M SORRY TO INFORM YOU THAT I'VE BEEN CHECKING YOUR **GOGO POLLS**... AND YOUR NUMBERS ARE **DOWN**.

I SEE. WHAT DO YOU SUGGEST I **DO** ABOUT IT... TO BECOME MORE **POPULAR?**

WELL, FOR A START, **LEND ME** TWENTY BUCKS.

FINE!! **IGNORE** THE **WILL** OF THE **PEOPLE** AT YOUR **PERIL**!!

I'VE TABULATED YOUR RECENT **POLL** RESULTS IN THE **GOGO** CATEGORY.

HOW DID I DO?

FRANKLY, YOU'RE NOT DOING TOO WELL WITH **KIDS** AGES 6 THRU 8, **MIELIE LADIES** AND **DOMESTIC** EMPLOYEES.

HOWEVER, ON THE PLUS SIDE, THE **"GRUMPY MADAM"** DEMOGRAPHIC **LIKE** YOU VERY MUCH.

SLAM!!

THIS IS **NOT** GOING TO **ENDEAR** YOU TO THE **KIDS** 6 THRU 8 CATEGORY!!

HOOT! HOOT! HOOT! HOOT! HOOT! HOOT! HOOT! HOOT!

HOOT IF YOU'VE HAD TEA WITH THE GUPTAS

©RAPID PHASE · 2018

HEY! WHAT ARE YOU **DOING**?! WHEN YOU SEE A POLICE **ROADBLOCK** YOU MUST SLOW DOWN!!

I DID.

©RAPID PHASE · 2018 www.madamandeve.co.za

AG, DON'T PAY **ATTENTION** TO MY COLLEAGUE! HE'S HAD A **TOUGH** DAY!

WOW! IT'S SO **HOT** TODAY! I SURE COULD USE A NICE **COOL** DRINK!

WHAT THE HELL WAS **THAT**?

GOOD COP. BAD COP. THIRSTY COP.

CLICK! CLICK! CLICK! CLICK! CLIC CL CLI CLICK CLICK

www.madamandeve.co.za

OOGA! BOOGA!

©RAPID PHASE · 2018

NEVER **MIX** GIN & TONICS WITH ALLERGY MEDICATION.

MADAM & Eve

BY STEPHEN FRANCIS & RICO

AND NOW... *LIVE* FROM **DUTY FREE** AT DUBAI INTERNATIONAL AIRPORT... IT'S THE SABC'S NEWEST AFTERNOON **TALK SHOW** --

"TEA WITH THE GUPTAS!!"

CLAP! CLAP! CLAP! CLAP! CLAP! CLAP!

SURE, THEY CAN **CAPTURE** A **COUNTRY**, BUT THEY **ALSO** KNOW HOW TO **CAPTURE** THE FLAVOUR OF **TEA**! PLEASE WELCOME **AJAY & ATUL**!

CLAP! CLAP! CLAP! CLAP! CLAP!

WE'VE GOT A **GREAT** SHOW TODAY, RIGHT AJAY?

THAT'S RIGHT, **ATUL**! LET'S BRING OUT OUR FIRST **GUEST**. GIVE IT UP FOR...

NHLANHLA NENE!!

CLAP! CLAP! CLAP! CLAP! CLAP!

NOW, NHLANHLA-- YOU RECENTLY **QUIT** YOUR JOB AS **FINANCE MINISTER**! CAN YOU TELL US **WHY**?

YES! I BELIEVE... IT WAS BECAUSE ...I FINALLY **ADMITTED** THAT I HAD **TEA** WITH THE **GUPTAS**!

CLAP! CLAP! CLAP! CLAP! CLAP!

EXCELLENT! AND CAN YOU REMEMBER **WHAT** TEA WE **MADE** FOR YOU BACK THEN?

I BELIEVE IT WAS **DARJEELING** WITH A HINT OF **CILANTRO**.

THAT'S **RIGHT**! AND WE'RE GOING TO SHOW **EVERYONE** AT HOME HOW TO **BREW** IT, RIGHT **NOW**! BUT FIRST--

CRASH!

© RAPID PHASE - 2018

INTERPOL!! EVERYBODY **FREEZE**! WE'RE **EXTRADITING** THE GUPTAS BACK TO SOUTH AFRICA!

WHAT?!

CLAP! CLAP! CLAP! CLAP!

HOW'S THE SHOW LOOKING SO FAR?

DO WE HAVE ANY **DARJEELING** WITH **CILANTRO**?

NOT TOO LONG AGO, THIS MANSION WAS A MEETING PLACE FOR THE RICH AND POWERFUL IN SOUTH AFRICA.

TODAY, IT STANDS EMPTY. A PLACE WHERE THE SUN DOESN'T SHINE.

THEY SAY THAT IF YOU COME HERE AFTER MIDNIGHT, YOU CAN HEAR THE GHOSTLY, MOCKING LAUGHTER OF THOSE WHO WISHED TO CAPTURE THE STATE.

JOIN US, IF YOU DARE.

...AS WE TRAVEL DEEP INTO THE BOWELS OF CORRUPTION AND GREED -- EXPLORING WHAT SOME SAY... IS THE "SCARIEST PLACE ON EARTH".

SAXONWOLD, THE HAUNTED GUPTA COMPOUND! --A CARTE BLANCHE HALLOWEEN SPECIAL!

HURRY! YOU'RE GOING TO MISS THIS!

MIDNIGHT! ...AS OUR CARTE BLANCHE GHOST HUNTERS ENTER THE DESERTED HALLWAYS OF THE HAUNTED GUPTA COMPUND!

WHAT NEFARIOUS PLOTS TO CAPTURE THE STATE WERE (ALLEGEDLY) HATCHED WITHIN THESE VERY WALLS?

WHAT CORRUPT POLITICIANS WERE (ALLEGEDLY) APPOINTED FINANCE MINISTER IN THE DEAD OF NIGHT BY...

AAAAAH!!

@☆#@!!

WE ACCIDENTALLY STEP ON A SLEEPING SECURITY GUARD!

THE HAUNTED GUPTA HOUSE IN SAXONWOLD...

CARTE BLANCHE'S FEARLESS GHOST HUNTERS PRESS ON.

IT'S SAID THAT GHOSTS AND VOICES PLOTTING STATE CAPTURE STILL ECHO THROUGH THESE DARK, DESERTED HALLS.

SUDDENLY -- ONE OF OUR PARANORMAL EXPERTS BEGINS ACTING STRANGELY.

HEH HEH HEH HEH HEH!

GASP! THAT FAMILIAR CHUCKLE! WE'D KNOW IT ANYWHERE!

HE'S POSSESSED! -- BY THE LAUGH OF JACOB ZUMA!

HEH HEH HEH HEH HEH!

I KNEW IT.

TROUBLE! WHILE INVESTIGATING THE HAUNTED **GUPTA COMPOUND,** ONE OF OUR CARTE BLANCHE **GHOST HUNTERS** IS...

...POSSESSED!

...POSSESSED BY THE **LAUGH** OF **JACOB ZUMA!**

HEH-HEH-HEH HEH-HEH-HEH.

THE **PARANORMAL EXPERTS** MUST **WORK** QUICKLY --

WE NEED TO PERFORM AN **EXORCISM** BEFORE IT'S TOO **LATE!**

HEH HEH HEH HEH HEH.

GET **PRAVIN GORDHAN** HERE, ASAP!

HEH HEH HEH HEH HEH!

THIS IS GETTING **GOOD.**

SAXONWOLD, THE DESERTED **GUPTA** MANSION, 00:30AM.

HEH HEH HEH HEH HEH.

GASP! HE'S **POSSESSED** BY JACOB ZUMA'S **LAUGH.**

ONLY **ONE** MAN CAN HELP US NOW!

...**PRAVIN GORDHAN!**

HELLO, MR GORDHAN? THIS IS CARTE BLANCHE. WE KNOW IT'S LATE, SIR, BUT WE'RE AT THE **GUPTA** COMPOUND...

...AND ONE OF OUR **GHOST HUNTERS** HAS BEEN **POSSESSED** BY THE SPIRIT OF **ZUMA'S CHUCKLE** AND NEEDS AN **EXORCISM.** HOW SOON CAN YOU--

CLICK!!

OKAY... PLAN B. WE CALL **JULIUS MALEMA.**

GWEN! YOU'RE MISSING THIS!

www.madamandeve.co.za

©RAPID PHASE·2018

19

CHECK IT OUT! MY **HALLOWEEN COSTUME** FOR NEXT WEEK.

...I'M **ROBIN' THE HOOD!** I TAKE FROM THE **POOR** AND **GIVE** TO THE **RICH.**

AND WHERE DID YOU GET **THAT** CRAZY IDEA?

THE **VBS BANK** LOOTING.

SO, YOU LIKE MY **HALLOWEEN** COSTUME INSPIRED BY THE **VBS** BANK SCANDAL?

WHO **ARE** YOU AGAIN?

HAVEN'T **DECIDED** YET. I'M EITHER **ROBIN' THE HOOD...** "I TAKE FROM THE **POOR** AND **GIVE** TO THE **RICH.**"

NOT BAD.

OR... "**I TAKE** FROM THE **POOR** ...AND GIVE TO **MYSELF.**"

TOO ON THE NOSE.

"I TAKE FROM THE **POOR** ... AND GIVE TO MY **BROTHER.**"

BETTER.

LET ME GET THIS STRAIGHT YOUR **HALLOWEEN** COSTUMES ARE INSPIRED BY THE **VBS BANK HEIST?**

YEBO.

I'M **ROBIN THE HOOD** FLOYD. I TAKE FROM THE **POOR** AND GIVE TO THE **RICH.**

THEN WHO ARE **YOU?**

FRIAR TUCK JULIUS.

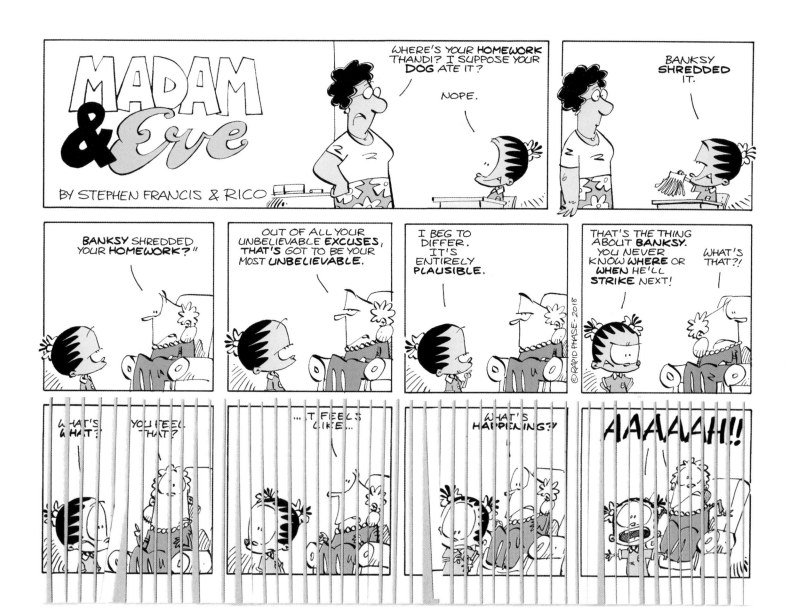

ENGLISH LANGUAGE QUIZ
<u>Question #1</u> Complete this well-known expression:
Rarer than _____

Rarer than *hen's teeth*
uncut diamonds

Rarer than *one honest*
politician

COMING UP TONIGHT...
"THE BOLD AND THE **SECRETIVE.**"

NEXT...
"SOUTH AFRICA HAS **SCHEMING** TALENT."

..."ISIDINGO, THE NEED FOR **SUBTERFUGE** "
... AND
"RHYTHM CITY **PLOTTERS.**"

AND WE'LL BE BACK WITH **MORE** OF THE **CONSPIRACY CHANNEL** AFTER <u>THIS.</u>

MADAM & Eve

BY STEPHEN FRANCIS & RICO

OKAY, CLASS...TODAY'S **QUESTION** IS... "*WHAT DO YOU WANT TO BE WHEN YOU GROW UP?*" --**THANDI**?

OUT OF SCHOOL.

GUESS WHAT? I **KNOW** WHAT I WANT TO BE WHEN I **GROW UP.**

WHAT?

A **LAWYER!**

VERY COMMENDABLE. HOW DID YOU ARRIVE AT **THAT** DECISION?

MOST LAWYERS HAVE NICE **OFFICES** INSTEAD OF **CUBICLES.**

UH-HUH.

ALSO, I'M REALLY GOOD AT ARGUING!

THAT'S TRUE.

PLUS, I WANT TO ERADICATE **INJUSTICE** AND AFFECT **SOCIETAL CHANGES.** TO **HELP** PEOPLE.

I SEE.

AND **THOSE** ARE THE **REASONS** YOU DECIDED TO BE A **LAWYER?**

TODAY'S TOP STORY: SARS PAID A **LAW FIRM** R 120 000 TO READ **ONE BOOK**, ACCORDING TO THE NUGENT COMMISSION.

© RAPID PHASE - 2018

WHAT?

23

AND, IN OTHER NEWS, ANOTHER **COMMISSION OF INQUIRY** HAS BEEN APPOINTED THIS WEEK.

AGAIN?

IN FACT, THE GOVERNMENT IS SO **CONCERNED** ABOUT THE NUMBER OF **COMMISSIONS OF INQUIRY** THAT HAVE BEEN CONVENED SO FAR...

...THAT THEY WILL BE APPOINTING A COMMISSION OF INQUIRY TO LOOK INTO **WHY** WE HAVE SO **MANY** COMMISSIONS OF INQUIRY...

AAAAH!

TRICK OR TREAT!!

AREN'T YOU A LITTLE **BIG** TO BE TRICK OR TREATING? BUT I DO **LIKE** YOUR "PRESIDENT RAMAPHOSA" **COSTUME.**

THAT'S BECAUSE I **AM** PRESIDENT RAMAPHOSA.

OH. UH... HAPPY HALLOWEEN.

SLAM!

IF YOU ASK **ME**... HE'S TAKING THIS "WALKABOUT" THING A LITTLE TOO FAR.

OKAY, FIRST-- GATHER LOTS OF **FOOD, WATER** AND **SHARP** OBJECTS... AND FIND A **SECURE, HIDDEN** LOCATION.

HOLD IT!

THANDI, BEFORE YOU CONTINUE...WHAT EXACTLY IS THE **SUBJECT** OF YOUR **SCHOOL REPORT?**

"HOW TO SURVIVE A **ZOMBIE APOCALYPSE.**"

ARRRGH...

NOT FUNNY.

24

Good morning, Mr Gordhan. Your mission should you choose to accept it....

...is to root out corruption and rescue all Parastatals including SAA, SABC, Eskom and Transnet, making them profitable again.

UH...

...YOU GOT AN EASIER WISH?

MISSION IMPOSSIBLE:
~~FALLOUT~~
BAILOUT

Coming soon to a budget near you!

SCARIER than HALLOWEEN.

More frightening than FRIDAY the 13th.

Job security was just an illusion...

...now their heads are on the chopping block.

Welcome to...

SABC **RESTRUCTURING DAY** *Who will get the axe first?*

Coming soon... to a television near you.

GOOD NEWS! WHEN I GROW UP, I WANT TO BE AN "INSTAGRAM INFLUENCER."

~SIGH~ WHAT'S THAT?

WITH MY CHARMING AND INFECTIOUS PERSONALITY, I'LL ESTABLISH INSTANT BRAND CREDIBILITY WITH A WIDE SOCIAL MEDIA AUDIENCE!

SLAM!!

I NEED AN "INSTA-GOGO INFLUENCER."

Stan Lee
1922 - 2018
Excelsior!

And remember, **you** can **contribute** one hundred, fifty... or even **one** rand.

HUH?

Help us **reach** our crowdfunding **goal** of **R3 billion!**

WHAT KIND OF START-UP NEEDS THREE BILLION BUCKS?

A NATIONAL BROADCASTER.

Help keep the **SABC** on the **air!** Only **R2,999,999,999.00** to go!

MADAM & Eve
BY STEPHEN FRANCIS & RICO

COUNCILMAN VUSI PANICS...

HI DAD. YOU WANTED TO SEE ME?

YES, SON. I NEED YOU TO **DELETE** A BUNCH OF **VIDEO FILES** FROM MY **CELLPHONE**.

...DAD? WHY AM I WEARING A **BLINDFOLD**?

NOT IMPORTANT. KEEP THUMBING TO THE RIGHT.

DAD -- I ALREADY **TAUGHT** YOU HOW TO DELETE VIDEO FILES.

I **KNOW**. BUT **THIS** TIME, I NEED YOU TO **DELETE** THEM SO NOT **EVEN** GOVERNMENT COMPUTER EXPERTS CAN **RECREATE** THEM.

GIMME A BREAK, DAD. I'M ONLY **EIGHT** YEARS OLD.

WHAT'S YOUR POINT? SCROLL DOWN.

DOES THIS HAVE **ANYTHING** TO DO WITH THAT "GIGABA VIDEO SCANDAL" GROWNUPS ARE **TALKING** ABOUT?

ABSOLUTELY **NOT**. KEEP SCROLLING.

OK. WHERE AM I NOW?

LET'S SEE. "VBS DEPOSITS," "SAXONWOLD SHEBEEN EXPENSES." ...KEEP GOING.

I THINK I FOUND THEM. FILE NAME: "PARLIAMENTARY PROCEDURE VIDEOS."

YOU'RE **PEEKING**! GIMME THAT!!

NICE GOING, DAD. YOU JUST PUSHED "**SEND**."

I **DID**?! WHO'S THE **RECIPIENT**?!

IT'S AN **EMAIL GROUP**: "TOP 20 WHITE MONOPOLY CAPITAL INVESTIGATIVE JOURNALISTS."

:GROAN: MY LIFE IS **OVER**!

...FIND THE FILE NAMED "**ONE WAY TICKET TO DUBAI**."

DAD! YOU PROMISED TO **PAY** FOR MY **UNIVERSITY**!!

©RAPID PHASE: 2018

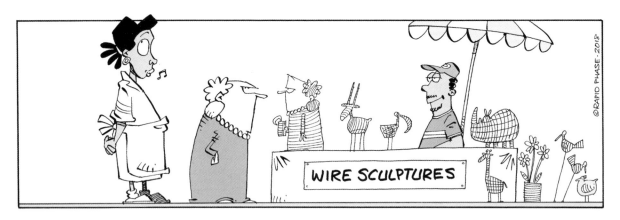

WIRE SCULPTURES

LOOK! THE HEATWAVE'S OVER!

IT'S SNOWING!

THANDI! ARE YOU FEEDING PAPER INTO THE FAN AGAIN?!

BRRRRR!!

... AND THE REASON YOU DIDN'T BRING IN YOUR HOMEWORK IS...?

WEATHER ISSUES.

≥SIGH≤ THE ECONOMY'S DOWN, PETROL'S UP ...AND EVERYONE'S TIGHTENING THEIR BELTS.

IT SAYS HERE... THAT PEOPLE EVERYWHERE ARE DOING ANYTHING THEY CAN TO SUPPLEMENT THEIR INCOME, NO MATTER HOW CRAZY.

WHAT WAS THAT?!

WHAT WAS WHAT?

MADAM & Eve

BY STEPHEN FRANCIS & RICO

CREATIVE GUYS WITH CARDBOARD SIGNS!

YOU ARE HERE

HELP! BANKSY SHREDDED MY

EX-ANN7 EMPLOYEE WILL READ FAKE NEWS FOR MONEY.

HOOT if you've had TEA with the GUPTAS!

NO JOB NO MONEY HAND OVER YOUR WALLET

LOOKING FOR A HANDYMAN? CALL MALUSI - A REAL "SELF STARTER" 099 555 0001

HOOT IF THE PUBLIC PROTECTOR WON'T STOP HASSLING YOU!

TAKE A SELFIE WITH SHAUN ABRAHAMS! ONLY 10 Rand

NO JOB. NO GUPTAS. NEED R10 MILLION FOR LEGAL FEES. HELP!

© RAPID PHASE - 2018

BOB's Electronics & Appliances

BLACK FRIDAY STATE CAPTURE **SALE**

AS THE **ECONOMIC FREEDOM FIGHTERS** CONTINUE TO LOUDLY PROTEST **PRAVIN GORDHAN** AND THE **STATE CAPTURE INQUIRY...**

...JOURNALISTS AND SOUTH AFRICANS ARE WONDERING...

...WHAT EXACTLY IS **JULIUS MALEMA** UP TO?

I HAVE NO EFFING IDEA.

MOM!!

TODAY'S TOP STORY... **PRAVIN GORDHAN** HAS LAID A DEFAMATION CHARGE AGAINST **JULIUS MALEMA** FOR CALLING HIM A "A DOG OF WHITE MONOPOLY CAPITAL."

...THANDI?

A DOG OF WHITE MONOPOLY CAPITAL ATE MY HOMEWORK!

WHAT?

30

MADAM & Eve

BY STEPHEN FRANCIS & RICO

HI. CAN I HAVE A HUG?

MY **FACEBOOK** FRIEND IN AMERICA TOLD ME IT'S "**THANKSGIVING**" OVER THERE THIS WEEK.

SO I THOUGHT WE SHOULD MAYBE ALSO TAKE A MOMENT TO BE **GRATEFUL** AND GIVE **THANKS** FOR EVERYTHING GOOD IN LIFE.

THANK YOU FOR THE **SUNNY DAYS**. THANK YOU FOR THE **COOLING RAINS**. THANK YOU FOR THE **BUTTERFLIES**.

THANK YOU FOR THE **FOOD** WE EAT. ... AND THANK YOU FOR THE **BIRDS** THAT **SING**.

AND THANK YOU, GOGO... FOR BEING MY FRIEND.

AHEM.

UH... YES, THANK **YOU** FOR BEING MY FRIEND ALSO.

... AND **MOST OF ALL**...

THANK YOU FOR **BLACK FRIDAY**, SO I CAN GO OUT AND **BUY** LOTS OF **THINGS** I DON'T REALLY NEED!

WOO-HOO!!

IF SHE EVER GROWS UP AND ENTERS POLITICS... WE'RE IN BIG **TROUBLE**.

©RAPID PHASE-2018

Panel 1:
AND IN OTHER NEWS... PATRICIA DE LILLE HAS SAID SHE IS FORMING HER OWN POLITICAL PARTY.

GREAT. ANOTHER ABBREVIATION TO LEARN.

Panel 2:
WHAT DO YOU THINK SHE'S GOING TO CALL IT?

IF I HAD TO GUESS... THE "APP." THE AUNTY PAT PARTY.

Panel 3:
OR... "INLBP." THE I'M NOT LEAVING THE BUILDING PARTY.

Panel 4:
OR... "NELP." THE NEVER-ENDING LAWSUIT PARTY.

MOM!!

Panel 5:
FANTASTIC BEASTS
THE CRIMES OF GRINDELWALD
A Warner Brothers Production

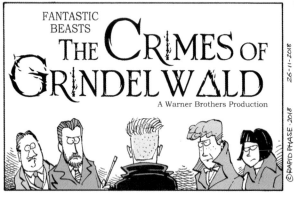

Panel 6:
FANTASTICALLY FLEECED
THE CRIMES OF SAXONWOLD
A Gupta Brothers Production

Panel 7:
THE MOVIE TRAILER FOR "THE LION KING"... HAS BECOME DISNEY'S MOST WATCHED TRAILER OF ALL TIME.

Panel 8:
"EVERYTHING THE LIGHT TOUCHES... IS OUR KINGDOM. ONE DAY, THE SUN WILL RISE WITH YOU AS THE NEW KING."

Panel 9:
DO YOU KNOW WHERE THAT CAME FROM?

AN EFF CAUCUS MEETING?

Panel 10:
UH... ACTUALLY, IT'S FROM "THE LION KING."

YOU HAVE TO ADMIT, MINE WAS A PRETTY GOOD GUESS.

MOM!

HI. ARE YOU AWARE YOU HAVE A **PAPER TRAIL**?

I SEE YOU'VE BEEN WATCHING THE **STATE CAPTURE** INQUIRY ON TV.

NOT REALLY. I WAS TRYING TO TELL YOU THAT YOU HAVE A **TRAIL** OF TOILET PAPER STUCK TO YOUR **SHOE**.

SLAM!!

THIS IS WHAT I GET FOR BEING **DIPLOMATIC**.

...ACCORDING TO WITNESS, THE **GUPTAS** COULD **SUMMON** PRESIDENT **ZUMA** TO THEIR **HOME**! ...AND WE'LL BE BACK WITH MORE OF THE **STATE CAPTURE** INQUIRY AFTER **THIS**.

WOW! IMAGINE ZUMA WALKING RIGHT **THROUGH** YOUR **FRONT DOOR**! WHAT'S THE **FIRST THING** YOU'D DO?!

SLAM!!

VERY FUNNY!

IN OTHER NEWS... JULIUS MALEMA AND THE EFF HAVE LAID A VARIETY OF CHARGES AGAINST PRAVIN GORDHAN.

INCLUDING MONEY LAUNDERING AND RACKETEERING. ADDITIONAL CHARGES INCLUDE ORGANISING THE JFK ASSASSINATION...

...THE FAKE MOON LANDING, OBAMA'S FAKE BIRTH CERTIFICATE, BEING A MEMBER OF THE ILLUMINATI...

...AND ONE OF THE SECRET REPTILIAN OVERLORDS CURRENTLY RUNNING THE WORLD.

AND IN OTHER NEWS, JACOB ZUMA SAYS...

...THAT "THANKS TO A PUBLIC MEDIA CAMPAIGN, HIS NAME HAS BECOME SYNONYMOUS WITH CORRUPTION."

THAT'S SO NOT TRUE.

...HIS NAME WAS SYNONYMOUS WITH CORRUPTION WAY BEFORE THAT.

MOM!!

DID YOU HEAR? PATRICIA DE LILLE ANNOUNCED THE NAME OF HER NEW PARTY.

GOOD.

OH. YOU ALREADY HEARD.

HEARD WHAT?

I TOLD YOU.

WHAT'S THE PARTY'S NAME? I DON'T UNDERSTAND.

"GOOD."

HUH? YOU'RE GLAD I DON'T UNDERSTAND?!

SLAM!!

IT'S GOOD!!

I'M SO HAPPY YOU'RE ENJOYING YOURSELF!

COME ON, GOGO. WHERE'S YOUR CHRISTMAS SPIRIT?

BAH, HUMBUG.

I JUST CHECKED THE CALENDAR. WE HAVE TO STAY IN SCHOOL FOR AN EXTRA WEEK LONGER THIS YEAR...

...BEFORE THEY LET US OUT FOR THE CHRISTMAS HOLIDAYS!

'TIS THE SEASON TO BE JOLLY! FA LA LA LA LA LA LA LA LA!

34

35

CRITICS AGREE THAT THE APPOINTMENT OF NEW NPA HEAD, ADVOCATE SHAMILA BATOHI, IS A SIGN OF POSITIVE CHANGES FOR THE PROSECUTING...

BAAAH!

WILL YOU KEEP IT DOWN, SHAUN!! WE'RE TRYING TO WATCH TV HERE!

BAAH, HUMBUG.

IN ENTERTAINMENT NEWS... TREVOR NOAH, HOST OF THE DAILY SHOW, HAS LOST HIS VOICE AFTER HIS RECENT VISIT TO SOUTH AFRICA... AND MAY HAVE TO CUT DOWN ON APPEARANCES.

"VOICE SHEDDING?"

COMING UP NEXT... THE DAILY SHOW, FEATURING TREVOR NOAH UNPLUGGED.

I SUSPECT ESKOM.

LOAD SHEDDING SCHEDULE

FLICKER

THANKS A LOT, ESKOM!

THANKS A LOT, ESKOM!

AND IN OTHER NEWS... FORMER **SABC** CHIEF OPERATING OFFICER, **HLAUDI MOTSOENENG**, INVITED JOURNALISTS TO A "HISTORICAL EVENT..."

I, HLAUDI MOTSOENENG, WILL NOW **LAUNCH MYSELF** INTO THE POLITICAL ARENA.

IS THAT A **GIANT CATAPULT?**

SPROING!!

www.madamandeve.co.za

WOW. LOOK AT HIM **GO**.

SEE WHAT ELSE IS ON.

©RAPID PHASE - 2018

SLAM!

IT'S SCHOOL HOLIDAYS!!

HUH?

www.madamandeve.co.za

WHERE'S GOGO?

SHH.

©RAPID PHASE - 2018

KNOCK! KNOCK!

WHO IS IT?

IT'S ME... FORMER PRESIDENT JACOB ZUMA.

GOTCHA! WE TAPED IT OFF HIS NEW TWITTER ACCOUNT.

www.madamandeve.co.za

IT'S ME... FORMER PRESIDENT JACOB ZUMA.

I HATE THE SILLY SEASON.

©RAPID PHASE - 2018

HO HO HO! AND WHAT DO *YOU* WANT FOR CHRISTMAS, LITTLE GIRL?

LET'S SEE... I WANT A BARBIE DREAMHOUSE, HARRY POTTER LEGO, GLOW-IN-THE-DARK HATCHIMALS...

VIRTUAL REALITY FATHER CHRISTMAS

Only R20

AND SO, *EBENEZER SCROOGE* WOULD BE *VISITED* BY THREE *SPIRITS* THAT NIGHT.

...THE *GHOST* OF CHRISTMAS *PAST* THE *GHOST* OF CHRISTMAS *PRESENT*... AND...

...THE GHOST OF *CHRISTMAS BONUSES!*

I HEARD THAT!

MADAM & Eve

BY STEPHEN FRANCIS & RICO

THERE WERE **THREE** OF THEM. THEY WERE VERY WISE... **STREET**WISE.

A SPECIAL **STAR** IN THE SKY TOLD THEM **WHEN** TO LEAVE...

...AND **WHERE** TO GO.

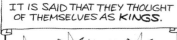

IT IS SAID THAT THEY THOUGHT OF THEMSELVES AS **KINGS**.

SO THEY BROUGHT BRIBES... UH... **GIFTS**, INCLUDING **GOLD**!

...ESPECIALLY **GOLD**.

www.madamandeve.co.za

AND THEN THEY REACHED **BETHLEHEM**, RIGHT?

NOT YET.

FIRST THEY WENT TO **SOUTH AFRICA**.

SOUTH AFRICA?! ...AND **THEN** THEY WENT TO **BETHLEHEM?!**

NOT EXACTLY.

©RAPID PHASE - 2018

WE'VE ARRIVED. **PARK** THE CAMELS.

WELCOME TO DUBAI

DUBAI??? ARE YOU **SURE** THIS IS THE STORY OF THE **THREE WISE MEN?**

ABSOLUTELY.

ONLY... I CALL IT THE **THREE WISE GUPTAS**.

MOM!

41

Panel 1:
WHAT'S WRONG WITH YOUR **ARM**?

I'M SUFFERING FROM "SELFIE-WRIST."

Panel 2:
"SELFIE-WRIST"?

IT'S FROM TAKING TOO MANY HOLIDAY SELFIES. GOOGLE IT IF YOU DON'T BELIEVE ME.

Panel 3:
LOOKS SERIOUS. CAN YOU EVEN **MOVE YOUR WRIST** TO TURN A **DOORKNOB**?

NOPE.

©RAPID PHASE · 2019 www.madamandeve.co.za

Panel 4:
SLAM!!

IT'S **2019** AND SHE'S STILL PRETTY QUICK-WITTED.

Panel 5:
GUPTA, GUPTA, GUPTA, GUPTA. THAT'S **FOUR**.

WHAT ARE YOU DOING?

©RAPID PHASE · 2019

Panel 6:
I READ IN AN ARTICLE THAT THE **MEDIA** PRINTED OR UTTERED THE WORD **"GUPTA"** 274 MILLION TIMES OVER THE PAST YEAR.

SO?

Panel 7:
MY GOAL IS TO MAKE IT 275 MILLION. GUPTA, GUPTA, GUPTA. THAT'S **THREE** MORE.

Panel 8:
GUPTA GUPTA GUPTA GUPTA GUPTA GUPTA GUPTA GUPTA GUPTA

WILL YOU **STOP DOING THAT**?! YOU SOUND LIKE A **PETROL PUMP**!

www.madamandeve.co.za 7-1-2019

Panel 9:
AHH. NO MORE **SCHOOL HOLIDAYS!** IT'S FINALLY **QUIET** AROUND HERE!

©RAPID PHASE · 2019

Panel 10:
... ALTHOUGH, TO BE HONEST, I **MISS** THANDI PLAYING AROUND HERE.

Panel 11:
BUT WHATEVER YOU DO, **PROMISE** YOU'LL NEVER **TELL** HER I **SAID** THAT.

I DON'T **HAVE** TO.

www.madamandeve.co.za

Panel 12:
TODAY'S **SATURDAY**.

YOU'RE CUTE.

LA COSA NOSTRA

LA BOSASA NOSTRA

YOUR TURN.

THREE! ONE... TWO, THREE!

RIGHT! I'M READY TO MAKE AN ACCUSATION!

IT WAS GAVIN WATSON IN THE VAULT WITH A HUGE PILE OF CASH!

DAMN. YOU WIN.

BOSASA CLUEDO.

Strictly ★ Come ★ Dancing South Africa

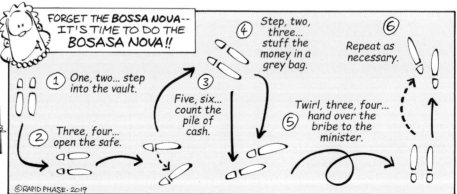

FORGET THE BOSSA NOVA-- IT'S TIME TO DO THE BOSASA NOVA!!

① One, two... step into the vault.

② Three, four... open the safe.

③ Five, six... count the pile of cash.

④ Step, two, three... stuff the money in a grey bag.

⑤ Twirl, three, four... hand over the bribe to the minister.

⑥ Repeat as necessary.

48

AND IN OTHER NEWS...

IT'S BEEN **EIGHTEEN MONTHS** SINCE THE "GUPTA LEAKS" BROKE, AND SO FAR THE **NPA** HAS DONE VIRTUALLY **NOTHING**.

©RAPID PHASE-2019

WHAT DOES **NPA** STAND FOR AGAIN?

www.madamandeve.co.za

"NO PROSECUTIONS ATTEMPTED."

MOM!!

DID YOU PAY **EVE** THIS MONTH?

I THOUGHT **YOU** DID. WHY?

LOOK OUT THE WINDOW. WE'RE BEING PROTESTED.

©RAPID PHASE-2018 www.madamandeve.co.za 5-8-2018

OUT OF MY WAY--I NEED TO MAKE AN URGENT DEPOSIT!

EMPLOYMENT DEDICATION WITHOUT COMPENSATION

PLEASE DON'T SAY MY NAME. OH **PLEASE** DON'T SAY MY NAME...

PLEASE DON'T SAY MY **NAME**. PLEASE DON'T SAY MY **NAME**.

www.madamandeve.co.za

KNOCK! KNOCK!

©RAPID PHASE-2019

COUNCILMAN **VUSI!** ARE YOU WATCHING THE **ZONDO** COMMISSION ON **TV?**

WHO, ME? NO. WHY? IS IT ON?

TIRED of hearing your name mentioned at the Zondo Commission?

Are you so worried that people might take away all your bribe money... that you can't SLEEP?

Well, now there's hope... to help you sleep peacefully, despite the ongoing allegations of corruptions.

© RAPID PHASE - 2019 www.madamandeve.co.za

ZONDO-GO... helps you zone out when the Zondo Commission gets too up close and personal.

ZONDO-GO

20 CAPSULES

*Ask your doctor if ZONDO-GO is right for you.

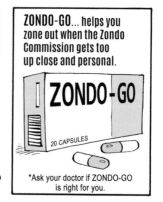

WHERE'S YOUR MATHS HOMEWORK, THANDI?

MATHS?!

WHO CAN THINK OF **MATHS** AT A TIME LIKE **THIS?!**...THE **ZONDO COMMISSION**... **STATE CAPTURE**...

...THE **FUTURE** OF OUR **COUNTRY** IS AT STAKE --AND YOU EXPECT ME TO SPEND **TIME** ON A **MATHS** ASSIGNMENT?!

© RAPID PHASE-2019

COOL. EPIC TAKE-DOWN.

THANKS. BUT THE **PRINCIPAL** SEEMS TO DISAGREE.

THE DAYDREAMS OF COUNCILMAN VUSI...

COUNCILMAN VUSI? I'VE BROUGHT YOU A **PAYOFF** FROM THE **GUPTAS**.

OKAY.

DON'T TAKE THAT! I'VE BROUGHT YOU A **PAYOFF** FROM BOSASA!

WRONG! **WE'RE** CAPTURING THE STATE!

© RAPID PHASE - 2019 www.madamandeve.co.za

TAKE MINE! BOSASA!

BOSASA!

TAKE MINE! GUPTAS!

GUPTAS!

THOSE WERE THE **DAYS**, MY FRIEND. WE THOUGHT THEY'D NEVER **END**.

50

MADAM & EVE

BY STEPHEN FRANCIS & RICO

COUNCILMAN VUSI... BLAH BLAH COUNCILMAN VUSI... BLAH BLAH BLAH... COUNCILMAN VUSI...

HEY, DAD! THEY'RE TALKING ABOUT YOU ON TELEVISION! I'M IMPRESSED!

DON'T BE. IT'S THE ZONDO COMMISSION OF INQUIRY.

WHAT'S THE "ZONDO COMMISSION?"

IT'S KIND OF HARD TO EXPLAIN.

A CRAZED, RACIST INGRATE EXEC OF A CORPORATE MONOLITH CALLED BOSASA HAS AN EPIPHANY...

HE GROWS A CONSCIENCE, THEN BEGINS MAKING THINGS UP ON TELEVISION ABOUT HARD-WORKING GOVERNMENT EMPLOYEES...

...FALSELY ACCUSING THEM OF CORRUPTION, KICKBACKS AND STATE CAPTURE... INCLUDING, UNFORTUNATELY, ...ME!

WOW. THAT'S INTENSE. ARE WE IN TROUBLE, DAD?

NAH. IT'LL ALL BLOW OVER.

© RAPID PHASE - 2019

BUT JUST IN CASE, WE MAY WANT TO LEAVE TOWN FOR A WHILE. GO PACK A BAG.

DAD? ALL THE SUITCASES UNDER MY BED ARE FULL OF CASH!

OH. RIGHT. TRY THE HALL CUPBOARD.

51

I'M REALLY **WORRIED** ABOUT MY DAD.

COUNCIL-MAN VUSI?

THE **ZONDO COMMISSION** IS REALLY **FREAKING** HIM OUT.

WELL, COULD HE BE **GUILTY** OF STATE CAPTURE OR ACCEPTING BRIBES?

MY **DAD**?! COME ON! HE'S AS **HONEST** AS-- HEY!!

HELLO, DAD? MY LUNCHBOX IS FULL OF **CASH**!

OH. JA. **IGNORE** IT. I WAS RUNNING OUT OF **STASH** SITES.

DAD? I'M REALLY WORRIED. MY SCHOOL LUNCHBOX IS FULL OF **CASH**.

I **TOLD** YOU-- I WAS RUNNING OUT OF **STASH** SITES.

DAD-- BE **HONEST**. IS IT... IS IT... FROM **BOSASA**?

ABSOLUTELY **NOT**!

WHEW.

I THINK **THAT** ONE WAS FROM THE **GUPTAS**.

ANYWAY, DON'T **SPEND** IT ALL AT THE TUCKSHOP.

I HAD A HEART TO HEART TALK WITH MY **DAD** LAST NIGHT.

COUNCIL-MAN VUSI?

YES. HE ADMITTED TAKING **BRIBES** BUT SAID **EVERYBODY** WAS DOING IT! EVEN **PRESIDENT ZUMA**!

LET ME ASK YOU A QUESTION: IF **EVERYONE** WAS JUMPING OFF A **CLIFF**... WOULD **YOU**?

DEPENDS...

...WILL MY **KICKBACKS** COVER MY **HOSPITAL** BILLS... OR DO I HAVE TO TAKE A CUSHY **GOVERNMENT** JOB?

YOU MAY BE **MISSING** THE **POINT**.

MADAM & Eve

BY STEPHEN FRANCIS & RICO

GOOD EVENING, EVERYONE!

IT'S TIME TO PLAY SOUTH AFRICA'S MOST POPULAR NEW GAME SHOW...

BLAME THE MEDIA!!

CLAP! CLAP! CLAP! CLAP! CLAP! CLAP!

LET'S MEET OUR FIRST CONTESTANT-- A CEO OF A BIG COMPANY WITH LUCRATIVE STATE CONTRACTS...AND WHICH HAS RECENTLY BEEN FORCED INTO VOLUNTARY LIQUIDATION.

CLAP! CLAP! CLAP! CLAP! CLAP!

IT SAYS HERE YOU'VE BEEN ACCUSED OF KICKBACKS, BRIBERY AND NEPOTISM. WHAT DO YOU SAY?

I'M INNOCENT OF ALL CHARGES! BUT I HAVE LEARNED A VALUABLE LESSON!

NEVER BRIBE A RELATIVE... UNLESS YOU'RE ABSOLUTELY SURE THEY'LL GIVE THE GOVERNMENT CONTRACT TO YOUR WIFE ...

... AND NOT AWARD THE TENDER TO YOUR SECOND COUSIN'S BROTHER'S FRONT COMPANY.

SO ARE YOU BLAMING THE RELATIVE OR WHISTLE-BLOWERS FOR THE "REPUTATIONAL DAMAGE" YOU'VE SUFFERED?

©RAPID RAGE 2019

HELL NO! I'M BLAMING THE MEDIA!

YES! HE'S GOING TO BLAME THE MEDIA!!

CLAP! CLAP! CLAP! CLAP! CLAP!

DON'T GO AWAY! IT'S OUR BONUS ROUND -- "BLAME IT ON SOCIAL MEDIA!" UP NEXT!

CLAP! CLAP! CLAP! CLAP! CLAP! CLAP!

PRESIDENT RAMAPHOSA HAS ANNOUNCED THE FORMATION OF A **NEW NPA UNIT** TO DEAL WITH **SERIOUS** CORRUPTION.

HUH?

SO PREVIOUSLY WE HAD **NON-SERIOUS** CORRUPTION? **SEMI-SERIOUS** CORRUPTION? **MIDDLING** CORRUPTION WITH A "GET OUT OF JAIL FREE" CARD?

SLAM!

...ASK A SERIOUS QUESTION.

MY REPORT TODAY IS ON THE CONTROVERSIAL SUBJECT OF "MONEY LAUNDERING."

MONEY LAUNDERING HAPPENS... WHEN YOU ACCIDENTALLY PUT YOUR **PANTS** IN THE WASHING MACHINE WITH **TWENTY BUCKS** IN THE **POCKET.**

IT MIGHT BE "HARD" CASH... BUT A LITTLE FABRIC **SOFTENER** SHOULD DO THE TRICK.

ARE YOU **SURE** YOU **RESEARCHED** THIS SUBJECT?!

WHY DOES EVERYONE KEEP **ASKING** ME THAT?

I'M ALREADY TIRED OF THE **ELECTIONEERING.** THE CANDIDATES AND PARTIES ALWAYS GIVE OUT **MIXED** MESSAGES.

MIXED MESSAGES? LIKE WHAT?

WITH THANKS TO MANDY COLLINS

MADAM & Eve

BY STEPHEN FRANCIS & RICO

WHAT ARE THOSE?

POLITICAL PARTY **ACTION FIGURES.** THE **EFF** IS HANDING THEM OUT. THEY EVEN **TALK**... JUST PULL THE **RING!**

HELLO. MY NAME IS CYRIL. WHERE WAS I FOR **NINE** YEARS WHILE THE STATE WAS **CAPTURED?**

WHAT ABOUT **THAT** ONE?

HELLO. MY NAME IS **MMUSI.** TELL ME WHAT YOU WANT AND THE **DA** WILL PROMISE IT.

AND IS THAT ONE IN **RED** WHO I THINK IT IS?

HI. MY NAME IS **JULIUS!**

LAND FOR THE PEOPLE! **JOBS** FOR EVERYONE!

HIGHER MINIMUM WAGES! NATIONALISE GAME RESERVES! VOTE EFF!!

TRY HELEN ZILLE.

TWEET! COLONIALISM WASN'T SO BAD. TAX REVOLT! TAX REVOLT!

WAIT A SECOND! HOW CAN THE EFF HAND OUT **ACTION FIGURES** OF ALL THEIR **RIVALS?** WHAT ABOUT **INTELLECTUAL** PROPERTY RIGHTS?!

INTELLECTUAL **PROPERTY** CAN BE **EXPROPRIATED** WITHOUT **COMPENSATION!**

LOOK. I EVEN GOT A **HLAUDI** ACTION FIGURE. WANT TO HEAR HIM?

NO THANKS.

@RAPIDPHASE 2019

IN TODAY'S TOP STORY... THE **ESKOM** CRISIS CONTINUES TO - -

Click.

WONDERFUL.

FIRST WE RAN OUT OF **WATER**... NOW **ELECTRICITY!** WHAT **ELSE** ARE WE RUNNING **OUT** OF?

INTEGRITY... HONESTY... SANITY...

MOM!

TAKE A LOOK AT THIS. IT JUST ARRIVED.

WHAT IS IT?

"WE REGRET TO INFORM YOU THAT TODAY YOU ARE IN **STAGE FOUR** PUNCHLINE SHEDDING."

PUNCHLINE SHEDDING?! WHAT THE HELL IS **THAT?!**

HALFWAY BOMBED

ROM-COMMED

UP NEXT... "WHEN HARRY MET SALLY."

ESKOMED

CLICK.

F-BOMBED

@#✳@#!!

MADAM & Eve

BY STEPHEN FRANCIS & RICO

HELLO, MY STUDIO GUEST TODAY IS AN **ESKOM SPOKESPERSON** HERE TO EXPLAIN WHY **LOAD-SHEDDING** HAS STARTED AGAIN.

BOO! @#%% OFF! HISS!

ARE THOSE DEMONSTRATORS?

RADIO STAFFERS.

GO ON. **WHY** MORE **LOAD-SHEDDING?**

WELL, IT'S VERY SIMPLE, REALLY.

IT'S BECAUSE OF THE LINGERING EFFECTS OF **STATE CAPTURE**, COAL AVAILABILITY CHALLENGES AND POWER STATIONS NOT GENERATING **POWER.**

ALSO, WE'RE IN A WEAK OPERATIONAL POSITION WITH CONTINUED **PRESSURE** ON THE NATIONAL GRID ...

... CAUSED BY US LOSING SIX ADDITIOAL GENERATOR UNITS, PUTTING ADDITIONAL **STRAIN** ON THE SYSTEM.

NOT TO MENTION ... THE BUDGETARY **NEEDS** OF MANY PARASTATAL PARTICIPANTS RESULTING IN A HIGH **MAGNITUDE** OF **FISCAL MISADVENTURE.**

©RAPID PHASE · 2019

... SO BASICALLY, GOVERNMENT **EMPLOYEES** AND **ANC CRONIES** TREATED **ESKOM** AS THEIR OWN PRIVATE **ATM**, SIPHONING OFF **BILLIONS** OF RANDS FOR THEIR **PERSONAL** USE AND YOU'RE NOW TECHNICALLY **INSOLVENT.**

STOP PUTTING **WORDS** IN MY **MOUTH**, DAMMIT!

Panel 1: IN OTHER NEWS, IT'S REPORTED THAT THE PRESIDENT HAS DIRECTED ANC SENIOR MANAGERS TO ATTEND AN **ANTI-CORRUPTION** "ETHICAL TRAINING COURSE."

Panel 2: THE **ANC** NEEDS TO SEND THEIR CADRES ON A **COURSE** TO LEARN HOW **NOT** TO BE **CORRUPT?!**

Panel 3: WHAT'S THE WORLD COMING TO?

Panel 4: YOUR **DOG** ATE YOUR HOMEWORK AGAIN?

YES, BUT IT'S **OKAY.** I'M SENDING HIM ON AN **ANTI-HOMEWORK EATING** COURSE.

Panel 5: COUNCILMAN VUSI?

YES. I'M HERE FOR THE **ANC ETHICAL LEADERSHIP** TRAINING COURSE.

Panel 6: BETWEEN YOU AND ME? I'VE BEEN REALLY **CAREFUL.** HOW DID THE PRESIDENT **FIND OUT** I NEEDED "ETHICAL TRAINING"?

Panel 7: ACTUALLY, **ALL** SENIOR **ANC MANAGERS** ARE SUPPOSED TO ATTEND. YOUR TRACK RECORD HAS NOTHING TO DO WITH IT.

Panel 8: GOTCHA! HERE'S **200 BUCKS.** FORGET WE **HAD** THIS CONVERSATION.

GO RIGHT IN. BETTER TAKE A SEAT UP **FRONT.**

Panel 9: HERE YOU GO, COUNCILMAN VUSI... TWO CHERRY SLUSH PUPPIES.

DAD! YOUR **PHONE** JUST BEEPED.

Panel 10: LET'S SEE... NEWS FROM THE **BUDGET** SPEECH...

Panel 11: AAAAGHH!!

BRAIN FREEZE?

Panel 12: SALARY FREEZE!

Panel 1: SAA PLEASE HELP! NEED TAXPAYER BAILOUT!

Panel 2: AND IN OTHER NEWS, **SOUTH AFRICAN AIRWAYS** HAS ANNOUNCED THAT IT WILL BE **SPLIT** INTO **THREE** SMALLER BUSINESS UNITS...

Panel 3: SAA PLEASE HELP! NEED TAXPAYER BAILOUT! SAA PLEASE HELP! NEED TAXPAYER BAILOUT! SAA PLEASE HELP! NEED TAXPAYER BAILOUT!

Panel 4: HMPH. DID YOU EVER NOTICE HOW SUPERMARKETS **PURPOSELY** DISPLAY **SWEETS** AT KIDS EYE LEVEL?

Panel 5: DID YOU **HEAR** WHAT I SAID?

Panel 6: HEY!!

Panel 7: I'M TALKING TO YOU! / HUH... WHAT?

Panel 8: I USUALLY SIT AROUND AND WATCH **TV**... OR READ THE **PAPER.**

Panel 9: THEN... IN THE **AFTERNOON** I TAKE A **NAP,** FOLLOWED BY SEVERAL **GIN & TONICS.**

Panel 10: I AM A SUBURBAN **GOGO.** THANK YOU. / CLAP! CLAP! CLAP! CLAP! CLAP! CLAP!

Panel 11: NEXT TIME, FIND SOMEONE **ELSE** FOR "CAREER DAY." / YOU SEEMED TO HAVE A LOT OF **FREE** TIME ON YOUR HANDS.

MADAM & Eve

BY STEPHEN FRANCIS & RICO

GUESS WHAT? I'M GOING TO BE A **LAWYER** WHEN I GROW UP!

THAT'S NICE. WHAT'S YOUR SPECIALITY? **CRIMINAL** LAW? **CONTRACT** LAW? **ENTERTAINMENT** LAW?

THE ONE THAT EARNS ME THE MOST **MONEY.**

WISE DECISION.

AND THIS IS MY **FIRST CLIENT.** I'M SUING **COCA-COLA.**

THAT'S GOOD. ALWAYS AIM HIGH.

I'M SUING FOR MILLIONS IN DAMAGES. HE'S BEEN **TRAUMATISED.**

HOW SO?

CAN YOU **BELIEVE** IT? THEY **REFUSED** TO PUT HIS **NAME** ON A LOUSY **COKE** CAN!

THAT'S **TERRIBLE.** WHAT'S YOUR **NAME?**

SEKGOLOKGOTJHANE.

EXCUSE ME. SORRY TO INTERRUPT. I'M LOOKING FOR **THANDI** THE **LAWYER** WHO'S **SUING** COCA-COLA.

© RAPID PHASE · 2019

THAT'S **ME.** WHAT'S YOUR **NAME?**

MAXIMILLIANUS.

MY REPUTATION ALREADY PRECEDES ME.

DID YOU BRING A **RETAINER?**

NO WORK

NO MONEY

NO CARD-BOARD

OKAY CLASS! **SCIENCE QUIZ!** YOU HAVE 30 MINUTES! BEGIN!

AWWW!!

QUESTION 1: "DESCRIBE THE CONDITIONS FOR A STAR TO BE BORN."

"WHEN **BRADLEY COOPER** BRINGS **LADY GAGA** UP ON THE **STAGE.**"

HI. ANYTHING GOOD ON **TV**?

WHO'S "STORMY DANIELS" AGAIN?

SO MUCH FOR "ENCOURAGING ENQUIRING MINDS."

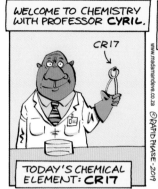

WELCOME TO CHEMISTRY WITH PROFESSOR **CYRIL**.

CR17

TODAY'S CHEMICAL ELEMENT: **CR17**

EXPOSED TO HOPE AND MONEY... AT FIRST IT **GLOWS** BRIGHTLY LIKE A **NEW DAWN**...

... ONLY TO **FIZZLE OUT** AFTER A SHORT TIME ...

Fizzle

... AND THEN **BLOW UP** IN YOUR FACE

BWOOMP!

I GIVE UP. **WHAT** IS IT?

IT'S A **GNU DAWN**. GET IT? A **GNU** DAWN.

"WILDEBEEST DAWN" JUST ISN'T AS FUNNY.

WHAT **ARE** YOU DOING?!

MY **CELLPHONE** SCREEN IS **FROZEN** ON **ROTATE**.

THE **JURRASSIC PARK** PERIOD... MILLIONS OF YEARS AGO...

...THE SKIES WERE **OWNED** BY...

...THE DREADED **PETROL DACTYLS!**

SOME PETROL DACTYLS WERE REGULAR...

...AND SOME WERE UNLEADED.

ARE YOU **SURE YOU** RESEARCHED THIS REPORT **PROPERLY?**

ABSOLUTELY. ...WHY?

WHEN **DINOSAURS** RULED THE EARTH!

NONE WERE MORE **IRRITATING** THAN THE FLYING PETROL DACTYLS!

CONSIDERED BY SCIENTISTS TO BE THE "**HADEDAS** OF THE JURASSIC PARK ERA"...

THE PETROL DACTYLS WOULD ANNOY OTHER **SLEEPING** DINOSAURS...

ZZZZZ ZZZZZ

...ESPECIALLY EARLY IN THE MORNING!

HADEDA!!

ARE YOU **SURE YOU** RESEARCHED THIS **PROPERLY?**

WHY DOES EVERYONE KEEP **ASKING** ME THAT?!

HOVERING OVER THE PRIMORDIAL SWAMP...

...THE FEARSOME **PETROL DACTYLS!**

NAMED FOR THE GREEK WORD "PETROL", MEANING "GASOLINE"... AND "DACTYL", MEANING "EXTREMELY EXPENSIVE."

AS THE SWAMP DRAINED, THE GREAT MIGRATION TO **DUBAI** HAD BEGUN.

THEIR LEADER? KING OF THE GIANT LIZARDS, THE DREADED **GUPTASAURUS WRECKS!**

HOLD IT RIGHT THERE, YOUNG LADY.

NOW?! I'M BUILDING UP FOR MY BIG FINISH!

Panel 1: AND SO... FOLLOWING THE **JURASSIC PARK** ERROR, CAME...

©RAPID PHASE - 2018

Panel 2: ...THE DAWN OF MAN.

HADEDAH!!

...OR, THE INVENTION OF **ALARM CLOCKS.**

Panel 3: ...AND THE **INVENTION** OF THE WORLD'S FIRST **SELFIE!**

www.madamandeve.co.za 9-10-2018

Panel 4: MY **TEACHER** SAYS SHE WANTS TO **TALK** TO YOU.

Panel 5:

©RAPID PHASE - 2018

Panel 6:

www.madamandeve.co.za

Panel 7: WHAT **ARE** YOU DOING?

Panel 8: BRAINSTORMING YOUR **HALLOWEEN COSTUME** FOR THIS YEAR.

Panel 9: YOU WON'T **BELIEVE** HOW **WEIRD** THESE **CELEBRITIES** LOOK LIKE NOW!

ARE YOU USING MY TABLET AGAIN?

@RAPID PHASE - 2019

www.madamandeve.co.za

Panel 10: AAAH!!

GASP!

Panel 11: **NOBODY** IN THIS **HOUSE** BETTER GET **COSMETIC SURGERY!!**

THANKS. WE'LL TAKE IT UNDER **ADVISEMENT.**

> slide to unlock

Loading... please wait.

Loading... please wait.

Cartoon unavailable. Please try again later.

BONK! CRASH!

BUMP!

MOM!!

WHAT'S EVERYBODY DOING UP SO EARLY?! IT'S PITCH BLACK OUTSIDE!

CLATTER!

CLUNK!

YOU FORGET TO TAKE OFF YOUR SLEEP MASK.

OH.

GAME OF THRONES
GLOBAL WARMING EDITION

SUMMER IS COMING.

GOOD MORNING!

I'VE BEEN MEANING TO ASK YOU... EVERYBODY KEEPS USING THE WORD "WOKE."

WHAT'S "WOKE"?

NOT **GOGO** UNTIL SHE'S HAD HER FIRST **CUP** OF **COFFEE**.

☺ MIELLLLIES!!

BEEP.

TWANG!!

DING!

Hahaha! MISSED ME!

BEEP!

THEY SAY LIFE WAS WAY MORE **EXCITING** BEFORE TEXTING AND SOCIAL MEDIA.

MADAM & EVE'S
DR SEUSS BOOKS
ON
STATE
CAPTURE

The CASH
in the HAT

HORTON hears a
WHISTLEBLOWER

ZONDO
COMMISSION

One fish
two fish
red fish
small fish

HAWKS

MADAM & EVE'S
DR SEUSS BOOKS
ON
STATE CAPTURE

GREEN EGGS
and HAM
...now cost 200 RAND!

BILL
R200

Oh, the Places
You'll Go!

DUBAI

...on taxpayer's money!

MADAM & EVE'S
DR SEUSS BOOKS
FOR
SOUTH AFRICA
2019

The RAT
in the
HAT

ZONDO COMMISSION

One phish
two phish
red phish
orange phish

UH... MAYBE YOU WANT TO RETHINK ASKING **THANDI** TO MANAGE YOUR **INSTAGRAM** PICTURE FEED.

MIELLLLLIES!!

YOU BOUGHT MIELIES?

WE CAME TO AN UNDER-STANDING.

AND IN OTHER NEWS... THE **LION** THAT **ESCAPED** FROM THE KAROO NATIONAL PARK HAS BEEN **RECAPTURED**...

...AND IS CURRENTLY IN A **POLICE HOLDING CELL** UNTIL HE CAN BE TRANSPORTED BACK.

THE **LION** THAT ESCAPED FROM THE KAROO NATIONAL PARK HAS BEEN RECAPTURED AND PLACED IN A **POLICE** HOLDING **CELL** ON A TEMPORARY BASIS.

HERE WE GO. THE OLD "GOOD COP, BAD COP" ROUTINE.

IN OTHER NEWS, THE RECAPTURED ESCAPEE **KAROO LION** IS **STILL** IN A **POLICE** HOLDING **CELL** AWAITING TO BE TRANSPORTED HOME.

KAROO LION? YOUR **LAWYER'S** ARRIVED!

ABOUT TIME.

CARTOON PANEL PHOTOBOMBING

FLOYD & JULIUS IN THE RUNNING OF THE BULLS IN PAMPLONA

I DON'T GET IT, JULIUS. WHY DO THE **BULLS** KEEP CHASING JUST **US**?!

MAYBE THEY'RE RACISTS.

WHAT ARE WE DOING IN A **TOY STORE**?

I'M LOOKING FOR A NEW **BOARD GAME** TO PLAY AT BOOK CLUB.

©RAPID PHASE - 2019

JISLAAIK! LOOK AT THIS: "GAME OF THRONES MONOPOLY." "BIG BANG THEORY MONOPOLY."

"DESPICABLE ME MONOPOLY." "WALKING DEAD MONOPOLY." ... IS THERE ANYTHING GAME MANUFACTURERS **WON'T** PUT OUT IF THEY THINK IT'LL **MAKE MONEY**?!

www.madamandeve.co.za

JUST IN: WHITE MONOPOLY CAPITAL MONOPOLY

WHITE MONOPOLY CAPITAL **MONOPOLY**

HADEDAH!!

©RAPID PHASE - 2019

www.madamandeve.co.za

VOTE FOR THE **HADEDA PARTY**

You thought the others drove FAST?

GET OUT OF THE WAY!

It's an election year! They've got places to go. QUICKLY!

THE FAST AND THE FURIOUS
ELECTION CAMPAIGN BLUE LIGHT CONVOY

VOTE FOR US!

Coming soon to a neighbourhood near you.

AVENGERS: ENDGAME DELETED SCENE

FUEL CELLS CRACKED. TRAPPED IN **SPACE**. OXYGEN RUNNING **OUT**.

I WAS HOPING FOR ONE MORE **SURPRISE**, BUT...

BEEP! BEEP! BEEP! BEEP!

NEBULA! A RADIO **TRANSMISSION** ANSWERING OUR DISTRESS CALL! WE'RE **SAVED!**

BEEP! BEEP! BEEP!

Don't waste your vote on a small party. Only the DA is big enough to keep the ANC and EFF out!

Please add me to your LinkedIn network.

MADAM & Eve

BY STEPHEN FRANCIS & RICO

AND IN OTHER NEWS... AFTER LOSING ANOTHER COURT CASE, THE EFF HAVE SAID: "IF JUDGES DON'T DO THEIR JOBS PROPERLY...WE WILL TAKE UP ARMS."

"...A BIAS JUDICIARY WILL FORCE US TO GO INTO THE BUSH. AND WE DON'T WANT TO GO INTO THE BUSH."

THE BUSH?

THE BUSH

JULIUS! WHAT ARE WE DOING HERE?

MANOEUVRES, FLOYD. MANOEUVRES.

BUSH TRAINING REQUIRES MOBILITY, CUNNING AND, ABOVE ALL, STEALTH.

WE MUST BE INVISIBLE TO OUR ENEMIES! READY? MOVE OUT!

HEY LOOK! IT'S THE EFF! WHAT ARE THEY DOING IN THE BUSH?

SO MUCH FOR "STEALTH." HOW THE HELL DID THEY SPOT US, FLOYD?

IT'S OUR BRIGHT RED EFF UNIFORMS, JULIUS! THEY DON'T BLEND IN!

GOOD THINKING, FLOYD. FIND US SOME GUCCI EFF CAMOUFLAGE UNIFORMS.

I'M ON IT, JULIUS.

© RAPID PHASE · 2019

LATER...

AH. THAT'S MORE LIKE IT.

HEY, LOOK! WHAT'S THE EFF DOING IN THE BUSH?!

DAMN! HOW THE HELL DID THEY SPOT US AGAIN, FLOYD?

BEATS ME, JULIUS. BEATS ME.

MADAM & Eve

BY STEPHEN FRANCIS & RICO

SWING VOTER ↓

...YOU GOING TO BE LONG? I'M HAVING FRIENDS OVER.

EVE... I NEED YOUR ADVICE. WHO SHOULD I VOTE FOR?

I MEAN, RAMAPHOSA SEEMS LIKE A GOOD GUY WHO COULD USE OUR SUPPORT... I THINK.

BUT IF I VOTE ANC... AM I VOTING FOR CYRIL'S ANC... OR SOME OTHER STATE CAPTURE FACTION?

THE DA? IT'S TRUE, WE DEFINITELY NEED A STRONG OPPOSITION PARTY!

... BUT LATELY, THE DA SEEM TOO BUSY OPPOSING THEMSELVES! ... AND DON'T GET ME STARTED ON THE EFF'S DIVISIVE RHETORIC!

©RAPID PHASE-2019

I'M SO CONFUSED! I'D PAY GOOD MONEY FOR SOMEONE TO TELL ME WHO TO VOTE FOR!!

MADAM-- YOU'RE A GENIUS!

I AM?

NICE GOING, BIG MOUTH.

WHO SHOULD I VOTE FOR? Only 50 Rand

75

DID SIPHO FALL **ASLEEP** IN CLASS?

DON'T WORRY, MISS. I'LL HANDLE THIS!

SIPHO! I GIVE YOU THE POWER TO **RISE** AND **AWAKEN!!**

IT'S A **MIRACLE!** HE IS **RESURRECTED!**

HUH?

MAYBE YOU SHOULD STOP WATCHING TV NEWS SO MUCH.

MIND YOUR OWN BUSINESS.

ARISE! ARISE!

AAAAH!!

HUH? WHAT'S GOING ON?

THE NEXT TIME YOU INTERRUPT MY **NAP**, YOU'RE IN BIG TROUBLE.

WATCH A GOGO RESURRECTION Only 10 Rand

I CAN'T **BELIEVE** IT! SOMEBODY **DO** SOMETHING!

WHAT IS IT, MOM? MORE **LOADSHEDDING?**

CRIME? CORRUPTION? UNEMPLOYMENT?

THEY **CANCELLED** "THE BOLD AND THE BEAUTIFUL!!"

AND IN OTHER NEWS... IT WAS RECENTLY DISCOVERED THAT A SOUTH AFRICAN AIRWAYS **PILOT** WAS FLYING FOR OVER 20 YEARS WITH A **FAKE LICENCE.**

UNBELIEVABLE! FAKE **DRIVERS** LICENCES! ... AND NOW FAKE **PILOT** LICENCES ?!

WHAT'S NEXT ?! A FAKE **DOCTOR'S** LICENCE? FAKE **LAWYER'S** LICENCE?

BEFORE WE GET TO THE **HOMEWORK,** ... DO YOU MIND IF I SEE YOUR VALID **TEACHER'S** LICENCE?

AND IN OTHER NEWS... **SABC** CEO MADODA MXAKWE WARNED THAT WITHOUT GOVERNMENT ASSISTANCE ...

...THE ORGANISATION WILL BE FUNCTIONALLY **INSOLVENT** BY THE END OF THE MONTH.

WHAT DOES THE "B" IN **SABC** STAND FOR?

"BANKRUPT." MOM!

MADAM & Eve

BY STEPHEN FRANCIS & RICO

OKAY, **YOUR** TURN.

HMM.

"**STINGY**." TRIPLE WORD SCORE.

THAT'S THIRTY-FIVE POINTS. **YOUR** TURN.

"**LAZY**." SIXTEEN POINTS.

"**LABOURCOURT**." LET'S SEE... THAT'S 21,22...

HA! NICE TRY. "LABOUR COURT" IS **TWO** WORDS!

MY TURN! "**LOAFING**." FOURTEEN POINTS!

WHAT'S GOING ON?

©RAPID PHASE-2019

WAGE NEGOTIATION **SCRABBLE**.

BY THE WAY--YOU **MISSED** THE DOUBLE WORD SCORE ON "**TIGHTFISTED**."

THANKS.

YOU'RE HELPING HER?!!

JUST SAYING.

Panel 1: GOOD NEWS FOR COUNCILMAN VUSI... LET'S SEE... "HAVE YOU EVER BEEN IMPLICATED IN BRIBERY AND CORRUPTION?" UH. YES...

Panel 2: "HAVE YOU EVER BEEN ARRESTED FOR A SERIOUS CRIME?" SIGH,...YES. "EVER APPEARED BEFORE A JUDGE?" YES.

Panel 3: "EVER CHARGED WITH A SERIOUS CRIME?" GROAN YES. "CONVICTED?" CONVICTED? WELL, UH... TECHNICALLY NO.

Panel 4: WAY TO GO, DAD! YOU MADE THE ANC PROVINCIAL ELECTION LIST! WOO-HOO! THAT'S GREAT! FIST BUMP!

Panel 5: ALRIGHT CLASS. ENGLISH VOCABULARY QUIZ. YOU HAVE 30 MINUTES. BEGIN!

Panel 6: "QUESTION ONE: USE 'ELECTORATE' IN A SENTENCE."

Panel 7:

Panel 8: "THANKS TO ESKOM, THE ELECTOR ATE HIS DINNER IN THE DARK."

Panel 9: HOOT IF YOU KNOW HOW TO FIX THINGS. Eskom

MADAM & Eve

BY STEPHEN FRANCIS & RICO

I'M NOT **RACIST**, BUT...

I'M NOT **EGOTISTICAL**, BUT...

I'M NOT **STINGY**, BUT...

I'M NOT **THIRSTY**, BUT...

WE'RE NOT **INCOMPETENT**, BUT...

WE'RE NOT **CORRUPT**, BUT...

VOTE ANC

HI! WHAT'S NEW?

WELL, USUALLY I'M NOT **GRUMPY**, BUT...

SLAM!!

HOW WAS YOUR DAY?

...A BUNCH OF "**BUT**" HEADS.

...AND I'M USUALLY NOT **JUDGEMENTAL**, BUT...

©RAPIDPHASE-2019

MADAM & EVE

EXPLAIN ESKOM, ELECTRICITY AND LOAD-SHEDDING

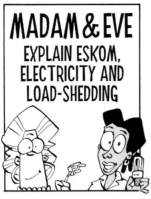

DC = DIRECT CURRENT

AC = ALTERNATING CURRENT

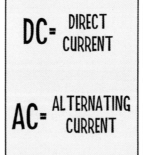

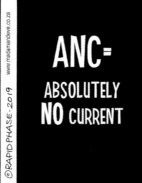

ANC = ABSOLUTELY **NO** CURRENT

AC/DC

ANCIENT ROCK BAND FROM THE 1970's THAT HAS **NOTHING** TO DO WITH LOAD-SHEDDING.

ESKOM. THEY MAKE ME FEEL SO **POWERLESS.** GET IT? "POWERLESS."

OH, LOOK. THE LIGHTS ARE BACK ON.

Z Z Z Z Z

...DOCTOR? HELLO, **DOCTOR?**

WHA...?

"**LOAD SHEDDING THERAPY.**"

I'M LISTENING. I'M LISTENING.

I DON'T KNOW, DOCTOR. **LOAD SHEDDING** MAKES ME FEEL A **LOSS** OF **CONTROL.** LIKE... IS TODAY GOING TO BE **LIGHT**...OR **DARK?**

WHEN YOU LOOK AT THE **DARK SIDE,** CAREFUL YOU MUST BE...FOR THE DARK SIDE LOOKS **BACK.**

UH, ISN'T THAT?

YODA, FROM "STAR WARS."

G#%@# **ESKOM'S** REALLY **GETTING** TO ME TOO!

WOULD YOU LIKE TO **TALK** ABOUT IT?

82

I RAISE MY GLASS TO THE "CAPO DI TUTTI CAPI"--THE BOSS OF ALL BOSSES!

...TO OUR NEW GODFATHER! TO OUR NEW DON!

"NEW DON." ...SO THAT'S WHERE CYRIL GOT IT FROM!

NOW WHAT DID YOU SAY?

BEATS ME.

CLASS...HERE ARE YOUR **MATHS QUIZ** RESULTS.

I GOT A "C"?!

THE ANSWER TO THE LAST QUESTION WAS 4. YOU WROTE "46."

IT WASN'T MY FAULT! IT WAS AUTO-CORRECTED!

YOUR ANSWER WAS "AUTOCORRECTED"? YOU WROTE YOUR QUIZ IN **PENCIL.**

MINOR DETAIL.

WOW, MISS...THOSE SURE ARE A **LOT OF PAPERS** TO **MARK.**

GO TO LUNCH, THANDI.

LET'S SEE... "QUESTION ONE: WHAT ENDED IN 1902? ANSWER: THE YEAR 1902."

SIGH.

MAYBE ONE DAY THEY'LL INVENT "AUTOCORRECT" FOR **TEACHERS.**

♪ DING DONG!

YOU SHALL NOT PASS!!

SLAM!!

WHAT WAS **THAT** ALL ABOUT?

LORD OF THE RINGS FANCY DRESS PARTY.

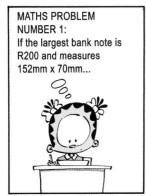

MATHS PROBLEM NUMBER 1:
If the largest bank note is R200 and measures 152mm x 70mm...

...how BIG a suitcase will you need to store R80 MILLION in cash?

"ASK *ACE* MAGASHULE."

≋SIGH≋ I WISH THERE WAS **SOMETHING** WE COULD **DO** TO MAKE SURE WE HAD **ELECTRICITY** ALL YEAR **ROUND.**

THERE IS.

SERIOUSLY?! **WHAT** CAN WE DO?

MOVE INTO LUTHULI HOUSE.

MOM!!

WHAT?! SHE **ASKED!**

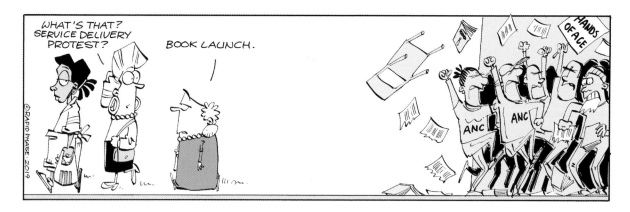

THANDI?

...WELL?

IT'S NOT MY **FAULT!**

...THE ANC YOUTH LEAGUE BURNT MY HOMEWORK.

POINTS FOR CREATIVITY.

THANKS.

Hello, Edith.

Greetings. My name is **Jacob**. A few years ago I was asked by my good friend and brother **Muammar** to cleverly hide 30 million US dollars.

Unfortunately, I am unable to move the funds out of the country at this time.

However, if you would be so kind to give me your **bank details,** I will gladly give you...

GWEN!

MADAM & Eve

BY STEPHEN FRANCIS & RICO

HELLO, EVERYONE. THANK YOU FOR COMING. IT'S NICE TO SEE SOME *NEW* FACES.

LET'S SEE... TODAY YOU'LL BE ATTENDING A *RIOT* IN *BLOEMFONTEIN*.

OH, GOOD. I *LIKE* BLOEMFONTEIN.

... WHAT WILL WE BE *PROTESTING*?

A NEW BOOK: "GANGSTER SKATE."

OH, SORRY. "**STATE**." "GANGSTER <u>STATE</u>."

B222T.

I LOVE BOOK LAUNCHES.

YES. QUESTIONS?

WILL THERE BE ANY *CHAIR THROWING*? I HAVE A *BAD BACK*.

NO. CHAIR THROWING IS *NOT* MANDATORY THIS TIME.

WHAT ABOUT *LUNCH*?

YES, LUNCH WILL BE SERVED. ...BUT ONLY *AFTER* THE RIOT ENDS.

AWWWW!!

© RAPID PHASE · 2019

NOW, I WANT TO SEE A REALLY *GOOD* PROTEST TODAY! MAKE ME *BELIEVE* IT!!

THE BUSES ARE WAITING OUTSIDE. BUT FIRST... LET'S DO SOME *WARM UP* EXERCISES. READY?

BURN THAT BOOK!!
BURN THAT BOOK!!

RENT A RIOT
CROWDS FOR PROTESTS & DEMONSTRATIONS

MADAM & Eve

BY STEPHEN FRANCIS & RICO

WHAT'LL IT BE?

VODKA AND CARROT JUICE, PLEASE.

HELLO. COME HERE OFTEN?

⁙GASP⁙ I DON'T BELIEVE IT! YOU'RE... Y-YOU'RE...

SHH! KEEP YOUR VOICE DOWN... IF I HAVE TO POSE FOR ANOTHER **SELFIE**, I'LL GO **NUTS**.

AGH... MY **FEET** ARE KILLING ME.

I'M SURE. ...OUT ALL DAY DELIVERING **EGGS** AND **CHOCOLATE**.

NAH! I'VE BEEN OUT **CAMPAIGNING!** I'M UP FOR **RE-ELECTION** THIS YEAR.

"VOTE **T.B.P!** THE BUNNY PARTY!"

THERE'S EVEN TALK OF **REPLACING** ME AS **HEAD RABBIT**.

REPLACE **YOU**?! ...YOU'RE THE **EASTER BUNNY!!**

LUCKILY, I HAVE A **WAR CHEST**. YOU KNOW THAT **30 MILLION** GADDAFI GAVE TO **ZUMA**?

⁙GASP⁙ ZUMA GAVE IT TO **YOU**?!

© RAPID PHASE · 2019

SURE. YOU **WANT** SOME?

HAPPY EASTER!!
LOOK-- THE **EASTER BUNNY** GAVE ME A BIG **CHOCOLATE EGG!**

⁙ HUH? WHA...?

JA, WELL, HE ALMOST GAVE **ME** 30 MILLION DOLLARS!!

GROWN-UPS. THEY GO A LITTLE FUNNY OVER HOLIDAYS.

I'M ONLY EATING **ONE MEAL** TODAY.

OH? WHY IS THAT?

I'M IN **TRAINING** FOR **EASTER** SUNDAY.

IF I'M CORRECT IN MY **CALCULATIONS**, WITH A HALF-EMPTY **STOMACH**... I SHOULD BE ABLE TO EAT **TWICE** AS MANY **CHOCOLATE EGGS** AS LAST YEAR.

AND SOME SAY KIDS THESE DAYS AREN'T **AMBITIOUS**.

WANT TO HEAR A JOKE?

WHAT DID **CYRIL** SAY WHEN HE **TOUCHED** THE **ELECTRIC FENCE?**

I'M **SHOCKED!** GET IT?! I'M **SHOCKED!!**

SHE TOSSED YOU OUT? I'M **SHOCKED!**

OH, SHUT UP.

MISTER PRESIDENT! **ESKOM** IS IN MUCH BIGGER **TROUBLE** THAN WE **THOUGHT.**

I'M **SHOCKED!**

UH, SIR? I DON'T THINK PEOPLE ARE **BUYING** THAT AS AN **EXCUSE.**

THEY'RE **NOT?** I'M **SHOCKED!**

MAYBE YOU SHOULD DELETE THOSE TWO WORDS FROM YOUR VOCABULARY.

REALLY? I'M **SHOCKED!**

WITH ALL DUE RESPECT, SIR. THIS IS **TRYING** MY PATIENCE.

IT IS? I'M **SHOCKED!**

MADAM & Eve

BY STEPHEN FRANCIS & RICO

MISTER PRESIDENT-- A FORMER PARTY MEMBER CLAIMS THAT *JULIUS MALEMA* IS RUNNING THE **EFF** LIKE HIS **BEDROOM, KITCHEN, TOILET** AND **YACHT.**

I'M SHOCKED!

... HE HAS A **YACHT**?

MISTER PRESIDENT... WE NEED A NEW **ELECTION SLOGAN**!

I'M BLOCKED.

HAHAHA! **CYRIL** CAN'T KEEP THE **TRAINS** RUNNING.!!

GASP I'M **MOCKED**!

SIR, SOMEONE JUST HIT THE **LIMO**!

I'M KNOCKED!

BONK!

I LIKE YOUR FOOTWEAR, SIR.

I'M SOCKED.

SIR -- I'M NOT SURE WE'LL BE ABLE TO KEEP THE **LIGHTS** ON.

I'M SHOCKED!

Eskom

YOU'RE **SHOCKED**! THAT'S IT, MISTER PRESIDENT! THAT'S OUR NEW **CAMPAIGN SLOGAN**!

SOUTH AFRICA: LET'S BE SHOCKED TOGETHER!

VOTE ANC   ANC X   **8 MAY 2019**

WHAT DO YOU THINK?

IT'S SCHLOCK.

Panel 1: AND IN OTHER NEWS, A FORMER MEMBER OF THE **EFF** HAS ACCUSED **JULIUS MALEMA** OF RUNNING THE **PARTY** "LIKE HIS BEDROOM, KITCHEN, TOILET AND YACHT."

Panel 2: **TOILET?** HOW COULD HE **RUN** THE **EFF** LIKE A "TOILET"?

Panel 3:

Panel 4: **MOM!** I'M LISTENING!!

GO PLAY.

Panel 5: OKAY CLASS -- SOCIAL STUDIES QUIZ. YOU HAVE 30 MINUTES. READY? BEGIN.

Panel 6: "QUESTION 1: WHY IS **HISTORY** SO IMPORTANT?"

Panel 7:

Panel 8: WITHOUT "HISTORY," GOGO WOULDN'T BE ABLE TO **DELETE** SITES SHE VISITED ON THE INTERNET.

Panel 9: DO YOU KNOW WHAT **TOMORROW** IS, MADAM?

IT'S **WORKERS'** DAY, EVE.

Panel 10: "**WORKERS' DAY EVE!**" YOU'RE GIVING ME **TODAY** OFF TOO?!

Panel 11: THANK YOU, MADAM!!

Panel 12: "WORKERS' DAY EVE." A NEW **HOLIDAY** IS BORN.

HEY!!

LOOK! THEY KEEP CALLING PATRICIA DE LILLE "**AUNTY PAT.**"

IT'S LIKE THEY'RE ALL ONE BIG **FAMILY!** ..."AUNTY PAT." ..."DADDY CYRIL." ..."UNCLE MMUSI."

..."COUSIN JULIUS." ..."BROTHER JACOB." LET'S SEE...**WHO** AM I LEAVING **OUT?**

"GODFATHER MAGASHULE."

MOM!!

I WAS THINKING. I'VE DECIDED TO GIVE YOU THE ENTIRE **DAY OFF** ON **ELECTION DAY**, EVE.

YOU'RE GIVING ME THE DAY **OFF** ON **ELECTION DAY EVE!**

THAT'S **TODAY!** THANK YOU, MADAM!

JUST A THOUGHT. EITHER YOU STOP **CREATING** NEW **HOLIDAYS** OR SHE CHANGES HER **NAME.**

HEY! IT'S **ELECTION DAY!** HOW COME I CAN'T **VOTE?**

BECAUSE YOU'RE A **KID.**

ONE DAY...WHEN YOU'RE **OLDER**...AND YOU GROW **WISE** FROM **AGE** AND **EXPERIENCE**...THEN YOU'LL **KNOW** HOW TO VOTE PROPERLY.

SO. **WHO** ARE **YOU** VOTING FOR, MOM?

I HAVE **NO** IDEA... **YOU?**

...NO **IDEA**, EITHER. MAYBE I'LL FLIP A COIN...

GROWNUPS.

MADAM & Eve

BY STEPHEN FRANCIS & RICO

SO... WHO DID YOU **VOTE** FOR?

I'M SORRY... BUT THAT'S ON A "NEED TO KNOW" BASIS.

AND **YOU** DON'T NEED TO KNOW.

YOU KNOW WHAT THEY SAY: "YOUR VOTE IS YOUR **SECRET**."

HEY! I'M **GREAT** AT KEEPING **SECRETS**!

COME ON! I **PROMISE** I WON'T **TELL**! IF YOU CAN'T **TRUST ME**... WHO **CAN** YOU TRUST?!

HEE-HEE. YOU'RE **FUNNY**.

YOU VOTED FOR THE **ANC**.

NO WAY! TOO **CAPTURED**!

...THE **EFF**?

...THE **DA**?

TOO **SCARY**.

TOO **CONFUSED**.

COPE?

THE **GOOD PARTY**?

TOO **HOPELESS**.

NOT **GOOD** ENOUGH.

ATTENTION, EVERYBODY! THE **VOTES** HAVE ALL BEEN **COUNTED** AND THE **ELECTIONS** ARE OFFICIALLY **OVER**!

AND WHAT'S THE MAIN **OUTCOME**?!

FIZZLE

APPARENTLY ESKOM **LOAD-SHEDDING** CAN START AGAIN.

I @#$@# **KNEW** IT!!

MOM!!

HELLO. **ELECTION HOTLINE.** HOW CAN I **HELP** YOU?

IT'S GOGO'S PART-TIME JOB. ANSWERING ANY QUESTIONS ABOUT THE **ELECTIONS.**

WELL...THE ELECTION'S **OVER.** I GUESS SHE'LL LOSE HER JOB?

NOT EXACTLY.

HELLO. ELECTION HOTLINE. SORRY YOUR **PARTY** DIDN'T DO SO WELL? NO BIG DEAL. GRAB A **GIN & TONIC** AND LET'S CHAT.

HELLO. MOTHER ANDERSON'S **POST-ELECTION DEPRESSION HELPLINE.** HOW CAN I BE OF ASSISTANCE?

SIGH... I'M REALLY DEPRESSED ABOUT MY **PARTY** DOING SO **BADLY.** WE HAD SUCH HIGH HOPES...

MMUSI...? MMUSI MAIMANE, IS THAT **YOU?**

UH... MAYBE...

PLEASE HANG ON A SECOND. I'VE GOT **MOSIOUA LEKOTA** FROM **COPE** ON LINE 2.

B222222T

I DON'T KNOW, DOCTOR. I GUESS I'M STILL A BIT **DEPRESSED** ABOUT THE **ELECTION** RESULT.

DIDN'T YOU THINK THE **ANC** WOULD WIN?

YES, OF COURSE...

AND THE **DA** WOULD COME IN SECOND?

YES, BUT...

...AND THE **EFF** THIRD?

YES.

SEE? THE ELECTION TURNED OUT EXACTLY AS YOU **EXPECTED.**

YOU'RE RIGHT. I FEEL MUCH **BETTER** NOW.

PAY ON YOUR WAY OUT.

WELL, **THAT** WAS EASY.

LET'S SEE...; CLINK; "BACON FLAVOURED SCOTCH"... EISH!

"WHIPPED CREAM TEQUILA."

CLINK! CLINK!

© RAPID PHASE - 2019

"BANANA & CINNAMON VODKA."

"COTTON CANDY GIN!".. YUCK!

CLINK! CLINK!

© RAPID PHASE - 2019

WHAT ARE YOU DOING, MOM?

I'M SHOWING SOLIDARITY WITH PRESIDENT RAMAPHOSA.

CLINK!

IF HE CAN CLEAN THE WEAK LINKS OUT OF HIS CABINET... SO CAN I.

IN TODAY'S NEWS... PRESIDENT RAMAPHOSA SAID THAT THE ANC HAS LEARNT A LESSON AFTER THE "PEOPLE SENT A MESSAGE.

© RAPID PHASE - 2019

THEY SENT A MESSAGE. THAT THEY WANT MORE JOBS!

THEY SENT A MESSAGE THAT THEY WANT AN END TO CORRUPTION!

UH, SIR? HAVEN'T THEY BEEN SENDING THE SAME MESSAGE FOR NEARLY 25 YEARS NOW?

POSSIBLY. BUT WHO TRUSTS THE POST OFFICE?

WHACK!!

© RAPID PHASE - 2019

ZING!!

HEY-- ONLY THREE DAYS UNTIL THE START OF THE CRICKET WORLD CUP!!

NOT EVERY-ONE'S A FAN.

SHE COULD'VE AT LEAST GIVEN US OUR BALL BACK.

ARNOLD SCHWARZENEGGER IN... *THE TERMINATOR*

I'LL BE BACK.

ARNOLD SCHWARZENEGGER IN... *SOUTH AFRICA*

OW!! MY BACK!!

KICK!

KNOW YOUR SOUTH AFRICAN TERMINOLOGY

KICKBACK

BOSASA

R

BACK KICK

ARNIE

G#☆#!!

MISTER **ZUMA**... SOMEONE FROM THE **GUINNESS BOOK OF RECORDS** IS HERE TO SEE YOU.

SERIOUSLY? SEND HIM IN.

MISTER ZUMA?

YES, HELLO. WHAT WONDERFUL **RECORD** DID I **BREAK**?

ACTUALLY, SIR. ...IT'S FOR **"THE LONGEST DELAYED CORRUPTION TRIAL EVER."**

UH... CONGRATU-LATIONS, SIR.

WOO-HOO! IS THERE A **CASH** PRIZE?

WHAT'S AN "OXYMORON"?

IT'S TWO WORDS **TOGETHER** THAT **CONTRADICT** EACH OTHER.

CAN I HEAR AN **EXAMPLE**?

... AND WE'LL BE BACK WITH MORE ON THE **ANC INTEGRITY COMMITTEE**.

BINGO.

MOM!!

www.madamandeve.co.za
© RAPID PHASE - 2019

102

READY TO WATCH CYRIL RAMAPHOSA'S **CORONATION** TODAY?

INAUGURATION, NOT CORONATION.

WHAT'S THE DIFFERENCE?

WELL, NO BIG PARADES, MOSTLY LOTS OF **SPEECHES**, AND **CYRIL PROMISES** TO DO A GOOD JOB AS **PRESIDENT**.

DOES HE AT LEAST GET A BIG SPARKLY **CROWN**?

SORRY, NOPE. **NO CROWN.**

SOUNDS **BORING**! I'M GOING TO PLAY OUTSIDE.

YOU DO THAT.

AND SO, PRESIDENT RAMAPHOSA'S **NEW DAWN** OFFICIALLY BEGINS.

I THOUGHT THE "NEW DAWN" **BEGAN** ALREADY.

THAT WAS THE **OLD** NEW DAWN.

SO, YOU'RE SAYING **FORGET** THE **OLD** NEW DAWN, THIS IS THE **NEW** NEW DAWN.

THE "NEW NEW DAWN." IS IT STARTING "NOW," "JUST NOW" OR "NOW NOW"?

SLAM!!

THIS IS WHAT I **GET** FOR ASKING A **SIMPLE** QUESTION.

THUMA MINA!!

THUMA MINA!!

I DIDN'T MEAN TO THE **PRINCIPAL'S OFFICE**!

PRINCIP

MADAM & Eve

BY STEPHEN FRANCIS & RICO

EVE -- HAVE YOU SEEN MY **MOTHER**? SHE HASN'T BEEN DOWN FOR BREAKFAST.

THUMA MINA!!

MOM?

SHE HAS A **TEMPERATURE**.

QUICK! CALL THE **DOCTOR!** TELL HIM HER **SYMPTOMS!**

THE **DOCTOR** WANTS TO **KNOW** IF SHE'S BEEN WATCHING A **LOT** OF **TV NEWS**.

TELL HIM **YES!**

THE **DOCTOR** WANTS TO KNOW IF SHE **WATCHED** THE **ENTIRE INAUGURATION!**

TELL HIM **YES!** EVEN THE **FLYPASTS!**

...WELL?!

©RAPID PHASE -2019

HE SAYS IT'S A CLEAR **CASE**. SHE'S SUFFERING FROM **RAMAPHORIA!**

SO?! WHAT SHOULD I DO?!

HE SAYS TELL HER **DD MABUZA'S** BACK... AND TO TAKE TWO **MALEMA TWEETS** AND CALL HIM IN THE MORNING!

IT'S A **NEW DAWN!!**

OKAY, CLASS... WHO CAN GIVE AN EXAMPLE OF **NON-FLOWERING PLANTS?**...THANDI?

UH...

PROTEAS!

INCORRECT. SURELY YOU **KNOW** PROTEAS ARE FLOWERING PLANTS! WHY DID YOU SAY **"PROTEAS"**?

I CHOKED.

"Where is the nearest Mielie Lady near me?"

TIC TIC TIC TIC TIC

"0.2 km west of your location on your street."

MIELLLIES!!

I LOVE TECHNOLOGY.

CAN YOU HELP ME WITH MY HOMEWORK?

SHOOT.

WHAT'S AN EXAMPLE OF **"DEJAVU"**?

AND IN OTHER NEWS, MANY OF PRESIDENT RAMAPHOSA'S NEW **CABINET** ARE STILL **CLOUDED** BY **CORRUPTION.**

BINGO.

MOM!!

WE'LL BE BACK WITH MORE ZONDO COMMISSION COVERAGE... AFTER THIS.

©RAPID PHASE - 2019

HEY. DO YOU KNOW HOW THE COUNTRY GOT CAPTURED?

HOW?

THE GUPTAS TURNED ON THEIR GPS AND HEARD: "TURN RIGHT FOR FREE STATE."

www.madamandeve.co.za

GET IT? "FREE STATE!"

GOT IT. GO PLAY.

KICK! GOAL!!

©RAPID PHASE - 2019

BONK! BONK! BONK! BONK! BONK!

www.madamandeve.co.za

THE WOMEN'S FOOTBALL WORLD CUP HAS STARTED!!

GO BANYANA BANYANA!!

Panel 1:

≋ SIGH ≋

Panel 2:

QUESTION ONE: GIVE AN EXAMPLE OF A "ZERO SUM GAME."

Panel 3:

Panel 4:

ESKOM'S BANK ACCOUNT HAD A HUGE SUM. NOW THEY HAVE ZERO.

Panel 5:

MADAM! YOUR CAR'S BEEN STOLEN!

RELAX. MOM'S USING IT. SHE STARTS HER NEW JOB TODAY.

Panel 6:

YOUR MOTHER HAS A JOB? WHAT IS SHE DOING?

WELL, IT STARTS WITH THE LETTER "U"

Panel 7:

UMBRELLA REPAIR? UNION LEADER? UPHOLSTERER?

Panel 8:

HI. ARE YOU EDITH MY UBER DRIVER?

SIGH.

Panel 9:

HI, MOM. HOW'S THE UBER DRIVING GOING?

SLAM!

I JUST DROPPED OFF MY LAST PASSENGER.

Panel 10:

I NEED TO LIE DOWN.

...MOM?

Panel 11:

MIELLLIES!!

Panel 12:

...AND THANKS FOR THE RIDE!!

Hello! My name is **Jack**.

Last week I went up a **hill** with my wife **Jill**... we wanted to fetch a pail of water. Ask Jill.

Hello, I'm **Jill**. Unfortunately, Jack **fell** down and broke his crown... and I came **tumbling** after.

We desperately need money for **medical** expenses. Please **help**! GoFundMe Jack & Jill.

THANDI! YOUR **HOMEWORK**?!

WELL... UH, YOU SEE...

HEY! I HAVEN'T EVEN **SAID** ANYTHING YET.

PREDICTIVE PRINCIPAL.

AND IN OTHER NEWS, JOBURG RESIDENTS ARE URGED TO **STOCK UP** ON **WATER**, DUE TO A MAIN PIPELINE BEING **SHUT DOWN** FOR REPAIRS NEXT WEEK.

GREAT. FIRST **NO ELECTRICITY** ...AND NOW **NO WATER!** WHAT'S **NEXT**?!

WE'RE OUT OF GIN.

AAAAAH!

THE
ECONOMY.

G#$%@!!

UNEMPLOYMENT
AND JOBS.

G#$%☆!!

LOW
GROWTH.

G#$%☆!!

SABC.

DOUBLE
G#$%☆!!

SAA.
ESKOM.

TRIPLE
G#$%☆!!

CRIME.
...EDUCATION
SYSTEM.
...ANTI-
CORRUPTION.
...NEW DAWN 2.0.

©RAPID PHASE · 2019

G#☆$%!!
G#☆$%!!
G#☆$%!!
G#☆$%!!

WHAT **IS** SHE
DOING?

...WATCHING THE **STATE**
OF THE **NATION**
ADDRESS.

G#☆%$!!

MISTER PRESIDENT-- WE HAVE THE FINAL REACTIONS TO YOUR **SONA** SPEECH.

...AND?

UH...MOST OF THE PEOPLE THINK THAT YOU'RE A **DREAMER?**

WHAT?! ...A DREAMER?

...WHERE DO THEY GET **THAT** IDEA FROM?

WELL, SIR...

...YOU MIGHT WANT TO RETHINK THAT **HAMMOCK** IN YOUR OFFICE.

SHH! I'M GETTING AN **IDEA.**

PRESIDENT RAMAPHOSA...WE'VE GOT TO **DO** SOMETHING ABOUT YOUR **IMAGE.**

WHAT'S **WRONG** WITH MY **IMAGE?**

WELL, SIR--THE "NEW DAWN" THING IS **FINE**... BUT **NOW** THEY'RE SAYING YOU'RE A **"DREAMER!"**

AND OF COURSE, THE **HAMMOCK** IN YOUR OFFICE DOESN'T HELP.

I KNOW, BUT...

OMG! LOOK! ON THE FAR WALL! CAN YOU **SEE** IT?! IT'S THE **BULLET TRAIN!!**

NOT THIS AGAIN.

HOW WAS THE **G20** SUMMIT, PRESIDENT RAMAPHOSA?

PUTIN'S ANGRY. HE SAYS WE STILL **OWE** HIM **BILLIONS** FOR ZUMA'S **NUCLEAR DEAL.**

OH, PLEASE. HE THINKS HE'S THE "GLOBAL GODFATHER." WHAT'S HE GOING TO DO? PUT A **HORSE'S HEAD** IN YOUR **BED?**

ACTUALLY... HE USED THE TERM **"BUFFALO."**

HE WAS JUST **JOKING.** RIGHT, SIR?

...UH, ...RIGHT?

YOU SHOULD'VE SEEN **TRUMP... ORANGER** THAN EVER.

HELLO, JACOB? IT'S CYRIL. PUTIN WANTS YOU TO PAY BACK THE NUCLEAR DEAL MONEY.

I SPENT IT ON LAWYERS.

WHAT... IS HE DOING HIS "GODFATHER" THING AND THREATENING TO PUT A "HORSE'S HEAD" IN YOUR BED? DON'T WORRY, HE ALWAYS SAYS THAT.

NOT A HORSE'S HEAD... AND NOT IN MY BED.

MORNING, SIR. WHERE'D YOU GET THAT NEW WALL DECORATION?

BETTER INCREASE MY SECURITY DETAIL.

HOLD ON A SECOND, JULIUS. YOUR BERET IS CROOKED.

EXCUSE ME?!!

OOPS. SORRY. SKEW. I MEAN "SKEW."

THAT'S BETTER, FLOYD. NEVER USE THE TERM "CROOKED."

MY BAD.

HOLD ON A SECOND, JULIUS. YOUR HAT IS SKEW.

THANK YOU, FLOYD.

TELL ME AGAIN, JULIUS...

...WHY DID WE DECIDE TO ALL WEAR BRIGHT RED BERETS AND OVERALLS?

IT MAKES IT WAY EASIER TO PICK US OUT IN ALL THE EDITORIAL NEWSPAPER CARTOONS.

SHREWD.

MADAM & Eve

BY STEPHEN FRANCIS & RICO

"A personal heartfelt message from your friend, Jacob Zuma."

GOTTA BE CLICKBAIT.

"Sawubona. Yes, it's **me**... the real **Jacob Zuma**. Heh heh heh heh."

"I've given so much to the people of South Africa... yet I am being **charged** with **corruption**."

"If I've done something wrong, can someone **TELL ME** what I have **DONE?**"

"Where is the **evidence?** Where is the **proof?**"

"Well, now is **your** chance to finally tell me what I've done. (And help me pay my **legal bills**.)"

© RAPID PHASE 2019   www.madamandeve.co.za

"Right here... on the official *JACOB ZUMA GoFundMe.com What did I do wrong?* website!"

"For only **R50** each, you can tell me what I've done and I promise to **think** about it."

"Hey! *Wait!* I didn't even tell you about the free **T-shirt** yet!"

GWEN! LEND ME 500 BUCKS IN BITCOIN!

FORGET IT.

WATCHA DOING, POP?

WHAT DOES IT LOOK LIKE? I'M GOING THROUGH OUR **TRASH** BEFORE SOME **JOURNALIST** DOES!

CHECKING A POLITICIAN'S **TRASH!** HOW **LOW** CAN THEY GO?

UH...WHAT IF THERE WAS NOTHING INCRIMINATING TO FIND?

I'M NOT **CHANGING MY LIFESTYLE** FOR A BUNCH OF **REPORTERS!**

YOU CHECK THE **COFFEE GROUNDS,** I'LL CHECK THE **EGG SHELLS.**

WHAT EXACTLY AM I LOOKING FOR IN OUR **TRASH,** POP?

ANYTHING WE DON'T WANT SOME NOSY **JOURNALIST** TO FIND!

© RAPID PHASE 2019

TRASH APPROPRIATION WITHOUT **COMPENSATION.** HERE. I MADE A LIST OF EVERYTHING **ILLEGAL** OR **INCRIMINATING.**

UH... THIS IS A **LONG** LIST, POP.

OF **COURSE** IT IS! I'M AN IMPORTANT **POLITICIAN!**

YOU **ALPHABETISED** THEM?

YOU LOOK FOR "A" THROUGH "P"... AND I'LL TAKE "Q" THROUGH "Z".

www.madamandeve.co.za

WHAT SEEMS TO BE THE **PROBLEM** OFFICER?

YOU WERE SPEEDING, MA'AM.

© RAPID PHASE · 2019 · www.madamandeve.co.za

THAT'LL BE EXACTLY **FOUR** COLD DRINKS.

EXACTLY FOUR COLD DRINKS? ...MAY I ASK HOW YOU **ARRIVED** AT THAT NUMBER?

SAVES TIME.

SPEEDING: 4 COLD DRINKS
OVERCROWDED
TAXI: 3 COLD DRINKS
JUMPING RED
ROBOT: 5 COLD DRINKS
NO LICENSE: 6 COLD DRINKS
ILLEGAL OVERTAKING:
       4 COLD DRINKS

"QUESTION ONE: DESCRIBE OUR POLITICAL SYSTEM."

© RAPID PHASE - 2019   www.madamandeve.co.za

"In South Africa we live in a DEMOCRAZY."

...DEMOCRAZY??

I GOT AN "A" IN MY SOCIAL STUDIES QUIZ.

THANDI-- WHERE'S YOUR HOMEWORK?

AHEM... I REFUSE TO HAVE HOMEWORK IMPOSED ON ME BY A CONSTITUTIONAL DELINQUENT.

© RAPID PHASE - 2019

THAT WOULD'VE GONE A LOT BETTER IF YOU ACTUALLY KNEW WHAT CONSTITUTIONAL DELINQUENT MEANS.

HEY, AT LEAST I KEEP UP WITH CURRENT EVENTS.

PRINC

HURRY UP, EVERYONE! THE ZONDO ZUMA SHOW IS ON!

© RAPID PHASE - 2019   www.madamandeve.co.za

THAT'S "ALLITERATION," RIGHT?

YES. PLUS IMPROVISATION FABRICATION AND MANIPULATION.

JUST HOPEFULLY NO VINDICATION.

MOM!!

THEY'VE BEEN **AFTER** ME FOR **20 YEARS**! I'M A **VICTIM** OF A POLITICAL CONSPIRACY!

I SEE... AND HOW LONG HAVE YOU **HAD** THESE FEELINGS OF **PARANOIA**?

WELL...

WHAT HE **MEANS** TO **SAY** IS... "HE CAN'T **RECALL**."

DAMMIT, JACOB! **MUST** YOU ALLOW YOUR **LEGAL TEAM** IN **THERAPY**?!

HEH. HEH. HEH.

MISTER ZUMA... WHAT EXACTLY WAS YOUR **RELATIONSHIP** TO THE **GUPTAS**?

I DON'T REMEMBER.

MISTER ZUMA... LET'S DISCUSS **STATE CAPTURE**.

WHAT'S THAT? I CAN'T **RECALL**.

WHY CAN'T HE **REMEMBER** ANYTHING?

IT'S AN AFFLICTION.

...HE'S SUFFERING FROM **ZUMAMNESIA**.

MOM!

I'M **INNOCENT**! I'M A **VICTIM**!

THEY'RE ALL TRYING TO **GET** ME! I CAN'T **REMEMBER** A THING!

WHAT THE HELL IS JACOB ZUMA **DOING** IN THERE?

MY **FAMILY'S** IN **DANGER**!

PRACTISING FOR THE **ZONDO COMMISSION**.

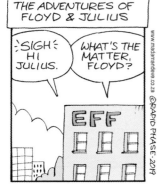

MADAM & Eve

BY STEPHEN FRANCIS & RICO

JULIUS! YOU'LL NEVER GUESS WHO'S ON THE TELEPHONE LINE!

EFF

PRAVIN GORDHAN?

WORSE. JACOB ZUMA.

JACOB. WHAT'S UP?

...IT'S ABOUT GWEN ANDERSON AND EVE SISULU!

MADAM & EVE?! WHAT ABOUT THEM?!

THEY'RE GONE! ...VANISHED! I OPENED UP THAT WEEKLY PAPER TODAY... AND THEY'VE COMPLETELY DISAPPEARED!

ARE YOU JOKING?!...MADAM & EVE IS THE ONLY THING IN THAT WEEKLY NEWSPAPER THAT I EVER READ!

ME ALSO!

WHAT'S GOING ON?

WORD ON THE STREET IS THAT THEY WERE "TAKEN OUT" BY A SECRET ROUGE UNIT OF WHITE MONOPOLY CAPITAL HIRED BY THE GUPTAS TO DESTABILISE SATIRE.

©RAPID PHASE · 2019

THAT'S IMPOSSIBLE! EVERYBODY KNOWS WE TOTALLY MADE UP THE WHOLE "WHITE MONOPOLY CAPITAL" THING!

DON'T WORRY, JULES. WE'LL FIND THEM! I HAVE EX-HAWKS MEMBERS GOING THROUGH THE NEWSPAPER'S TRASH EVEN AS WE SPEAK!

GOOD! GET BACK TO ME.

MEANWHILE... AT THE DAILY MAVERICK...

EVE!! HAS ANYBODY UNPACKED MY GIN & TONIC BOXES YET?!

MIELLLIES!

SOMETHING WRONG, MADAM?

THAT'S ODD. I COULD SWEAR I JUST SAW ZAPIRO ACROSS THE STREET BUYING MIELIES JUST NOW.

GET OUT OF THE WAY, SLOW POKES!

BEEP! BEEP!

SCREECH!

©RAPID PHASE - 2019   www.madamandeve.co.za

IT'S THE LATEST THING IN **SENIOR CITIZEN MOBILITY**: A "GOGO-GO." COMES WITH GPS... MP3... CELLPHONE CHARGER...

WHAT'S THAT?

I **ADDED** THAT MYSELF. IT'S A **GIN & TONIC** CUP HOLDER!

SORRY! GOTTA GO-GO!

HEY!! YOU'RE NOT SUPPOSED TO DRINK AND DRIVE!!

WHIRRR!

BORN TO BE WILD!!

©RAPID PHASE - 2019   www.madamandeve.co.za

GET YOUR MOTOR RUNNIN'

GOGO-GO™ DIGITAL SCOOTERS... THE LATEST THING IN **SENIOR CITIZEN MOBILITY.**

LOOK WHAT I LEARNED AT SCHOOL TODAY. I **PHOTOCOPIED** A TEN RAND NOTE, THEN COLOURED IT **GREEN!**

HUH?!

©RAPID PHASE - 2019

WHAT KIND OF **CLASS** TEACHES YOU HOW TO MAKE **COUNTERFEIT MONEY?!**

"ARTS AND GRAFT."

www.madamandeve.co.za

SLAM!

..., WELL, I THOUGHT IT WAS PRETTY **FUNNY.**

THE PUBLIC PROTECTOR

INVESTIGATE **GORDHAN!**

THE HOMEWORK PROTECTOR

IT'S NOT HER FAULT... HER **DOG** ATE IT.

THE MIELIE LADY PROTECTOR

MIELLLIES!

THE POLICE ROADBLOCK PROTECTOR

BUSISIWE -- WHAT SHOULD WE DO ABOUT THIS **ROGUE** UNIT?

CHARGE GORDHAN!

THE OFFICE OF THE PUBLIC PROTECTOR

STATE CAPTURE?

CHARGE GORDHAN!

CLIMATE CHANGE?

CHARGE GORDHAN!

THE OFFICE OF THE PUBLIC PROTECTOR

JUSTICE WILL BE **SERVED!**

THE OFFICE OF THE PUBLIC PROTECTOR

THAT **REMINDS** ME, WHO'S **PAYING** FOR **LUNCH?**

CHARGE GORDHAN!

THE OFFICE OF THE PUBLIC PROTECTOR

...IN YET **ANOTHER** SCATHING **MONDAY JUDGEMENT,** PUBLIC PROTECTOR BUSISIWE MKHWEBANE WAS HANDED A FURTHER HUMILIATING **DEFEAT** IN THE HIGH COURT...

AT LEAST WE KNOW **ONE** THING ABOUT THE PUBLIC PROTECTOR.

WHAT'S THAT?

SHE MUST REALLY **HATE** MONDAYS.

GOOD ONE.

I THOUGHT SO.

THIS WHOLE **PUBLIC PROTECTOR** THING IS SO **CONFUSING!**

LET ME TRY AND EXPLAIN.

IT'S **CR** AND **PG** VS THE **PP**, WHO IS SUPPORTED BY THE **EFF** AND **JZ** AFTER A COMPLAINT BY THE **DA** AND NOW INVOLVES THE **NPA, ABSA, SARS** AND **CR17.**

THANKS A **LOT!** NOW I'M EVEN **MORE** CONFUSED!

YOU'RE WELCOME.

AND IN OTHER NEWS, **ESKOM MANAGERS** WARN THAT UNLESS THEY GET SALARY INCREASES AND BONUSES... **LOAD SHEDDING** MAY OCCUR!

WHAT?! THAT'S **BLACKMAIL!!** THAT'S **OUTRAGEOUS!**

THAT'S-- THAT'S--

WELL... MAYBE WE SHOULDN'T RUSH TO JUDGEMENT.

MOM!!

WHAT?! MY ICE CUBES ARE MELTING!

DO YOU BELIEVE IN RECYCLING FREEDOM?

HUH? "RECYCLING"?

NO, MON. I HATE RECYCLING.

YOU... **HATE** RECYCLING?

JA, MON.

...ESPECIALLY WHEN I FORGET TO USE BOTH **CHAINS** AND SOME **TSOTSI** STEALS MY **BIKE!**

MADAM & Eve

BY STEPHEN FRANCIS & RICO

RIGHT! **MY TURN!** ARE YOU **READY?**

GO FOR IT, GOGO!

≳RATTLE≲ ≳RATTLE≲

#@#!

THREE! ONE, TWO... **THREE!**

OKAY! I'M READY TO MAKE AN **ACCUSATION!**

ALREADY?! I HAVEN'T EVEN HAD A **TURN** YET!

≳AHEM≲ LET'S SEE... I SAY...

...IT WAS PRAVIN GORDHAN ...WITH THE **ROGUE** UNIT IN THE **DINING ROOM!**

...AND THE **LOUNGE,** THE **KITCHEN,** THE **STUDY,** THE **HALL,** THE **BILLIARD ROOM...**

...THE **CONSERVATORY,** THE **BALL ROOM,** THE **LIBRARY** AND THE **CELLAR!**

©RAPID PHASE-2019

WOW THAT'S ...ER, ALL **INCORRECT.** YOU LOSE!

WHAT?! **AGAIN?!**

WHAT ARE YOU **PLAYING?**

PUBLIC PROTECTOR CLUEDO.

YES, THANDI?

MISS-- I HAVE HERE A BATCH OF **LEAKED EMAILS** THAT **PROVE...**

© RAPID PHASE - 2019

...THAT THERE'S A **CONSPIRACY** OF **TEACHERS** PLOTTING TO GIVE OUT **MORE HOMEWORK** THAN NECESSARY!

LET ME SEE THOSE!

THESE ARE WRITTEN IN **PENCIL** AND **CRAYONS**.

R-REALLY? I DIDN'T EVEN NOTICE.

www.madamandeve.co.za

THE DEVIL IS IN THE DETAILS.

OH, SHUT UP.

AND IN OTHER NEWS... **PUBLIC PROTECTOR** BUSISIWE MKHWEBANE HAS **LOST** ANOTHER IMPORTANT **CASE**.

AGAIN?

© RAPID PHASE - 2019

GEE. THE PUBLIC PROTECTOR **LOSES** MORE...

...LOSES **MORE** THAN...THAN...

www.madamandeve.co.za

BAFANA BAFANA AND THE WORLD CUP **PROTEAS** COMBINED.

MOM!!

DING DONG! ♪

WHO IS IT?

© RAPID PHASE - 2019

IT'S JACOB ZUMA! **DEREK HANEKOM** IS **SUING** ME FOR DEFAMATION AND HIS **LAWYERS** ARE TRYING TO **SERVE** ME WITH **PAPERS!** YOU'VE GOT TO **HIDE** ME!

www.madamandeve.co.za

WHAT'S IN IT FOR **ME?**

HOW ABOUT A GUIDED TOUR OF **NKANDLA?**

GWEN! YOU WANT TO **SEE** NKANDLA?

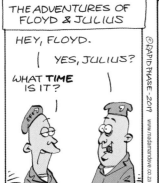

PLEASE! IT'S **JACOB ZUMA!** DEREK HANEKOM'S **LAWYERS** ARE LOOKING FOR ME! I NEED A PLACE TO **HIDE.**

©RAPID PHASE · 2019   www.madamandeve.co.za

HOW DO I **KNOW** IT'S REALLY **YOU**... JACOB ZUMA.

ASK ME A **MATHS** QUESTION.

HOW MUCH IS **SIX** PLUS **SEVEN?**

ELEVENTY.

OKAY. IT'S **YOU.** I'M OPENING THE **DOOR.**

LET ME IN! IT'S **JACOB ZUMA!** DEREK HANEKOM'S **LAWYERS** ARE LOOKING FOR ME! I NEED A PLACE TO **HIDE!**

SIGH.

©RAPID PHASE · 2019   www.madamandeve.co.za

THANK YOU, KIND WHITE GOGO.

WHY DO THESE THINGS ALWAYS HAPPEN TO **ME?**

WHERE SHALL I **HIDE?**

UH... MAYBE STAND OVER **THERE.**

NEW LAMP?

REFURBISHED.

AND IN OTHER NEWS... IN ORDER TO **AVOID** BEING SERVED **COURT** PAPERS, **JACOB ZUMA** HAS BEEN "LAYING LOW."

©RAPID PHASE · 2019

IT IS BELIEVED HE IS **HIDING** SOMEWHERE IN THE **SUBURBS**... BUT EXACTLY **WHERE**... IS ANYONE'S GUESS.

ARE YOU **SURE** YOU LIKE THAT NEW **LAMP?**

IT GROWS ON YOU.

THAT GIN & TONIC LOOKS **GOOD.**

SHH.

MADAM & Eve

BY STEPHEN FRANCIS & RICO

AND IN OTHER NEWS... AS A NEW SEASON OF ENDLESS **COURT CASES** BEGINS, TWO **MORE** FORMER MINISTERS HAVE JOINED DEREK HANEKOM IN FILING **DEFAMATION LAWSUITS** AGAINST EX-PRESIDENT JACOB ZUMA...

OUR LAWSUITS AND MOTIONS GO VIRAL ON TWITTER...

LAW OFFICES

... SERVING COURT **PAPERS** ON ZUMA WHO'S **BITTER.**

LAW OFFICES

WE'RE AFTER HIS **MONEY** AND ALL OF HIS **BLINGS...**

LAW OFFICES

THESE ARE A **FEW** OF OUR **FAVOURITE THINGS!**

THE **PP** WHO LOSES SO MUCH THAT SHE'S **FUNNY...**

BONK!

APPEALS AND POSTPONEMENTS THAT MAKE **TONS** OF **MONEY...**

WE BUY HOUSES AND PORSCHES AND BIG DIAMOND **RINGS...**

THESE ARE A FEW OF OUR **FAVOURITE THINGS!**

I'M GONNA BE A **LAWYER** WHEN I GROW UP.

GOOD CALL.

MIELLLLIES!

SIRI? WHERE DID I PUT MY **KATTY**?

End table. Top drawer.

SIRI? TELL ME WHEN TO **DUCK**.

You **got** it!

TRAITOR!

Think of me as neutral... the **Switzerland** of virtual assistants.

"KARABO MATHEBE"?

Ding

I GOT A FACEBOOK **FRIEND** REQUEST FROM "KARABO MATHEBE". DOES ANYONE **KNOW** A "KARABO MATHEBE"?

THAT'S **ME**!!

MIELLLLLIES!!

AWWWW!

AND IN OTHER NEWS... HERE'S A NEW STATISTIC FROM THE **JOHANNESBURG METRO POLICE DEPARTMENT**...

...IN THE MONTH OF JULY THIS YEAR, **873 560 SPEEDING FINES** WERE ISSUED.

WOW. 873 560... THAT'S A **LOT** OF SPEEDING TICKETS.

HOW MUCH IS THAT IN **COLD DRINKS**?

MADAM & Eve

BY STEPHEN FRANCIS & RICO

THIS WEEK'S TOP STORY... **BOSASA** CEO **GAVIN WATSON**, IMPLICATED AT THE **ZONDO COMMISSION** INTO **STATE CAPTURE**...WAS **KILLED** WHEN HE **ALLEGEDLY** LOST CONTROL OF HIS **CAR** AND **CRASHED** INTO A CONCRETE PILLAR.

"ALLEGEDLY."

ALLEGEDLY?

SHE'S SAYING THE **CONSPIRACY THEORISTS** ARE GOING CRAZY ON THE INTERNET.

HOW MANY **REAL** CONSPIRACIES **ARE** THERE?

OH, **TONS.**

YOU KNOW THE (SO-CALLED) "**MOON LANDINGS**"?

JA?

FAKE. DONE ON A **MOVIE SET.**

NO!

JA?

IT'S TRUE. THE **9-11** TERRORIST PLANE **CRASHES** IN AMERICA?

INSIDE JOB.

AREA 51 AND THE **ALIENS**? **SECRET** SOCIETIES THAT **CONTROL** THE WORLD? ...ALL TOTALLY **TRUE.**

WHAT ABOUT **ELVIS**?

ALIVE AND WELL AND LIVING IN BENONI.

NOT SO FAST! WHAT ABOUT **BIGFOOT**?

WELL, THEY **CAUGHT** HIM... BUT HE'S BEEN **CRYOGENICALLY FROZEN.**

© RAPID PHASE 2019

≤GASP≥ ...AND **WHITE MONOPOLY CAPITAL**?!

DUH.

SO **JACOB ZUMA** IS **RIGHT!** EVERYBODY IS OUT TO GET HIM!

I KNOW I AM.

MOM!!

MADAM & Eve
BY STEPHEN FRANCIS & RICO

NEW SOUTH AFRICAN PRODUCT LINES

MALEMANADE

...when life gives you lemons... make MALEMANADE!

MALEMA NADE!

Steve HOFMAYO

...FOR THE TASTE YOU CAN'T RACIST!

Steve HOFMAYO
CREAMY WHITE AND BITTER

©RAPID PHASE - 2019

ACE OF ♠ SHADES

The sunglasses for really shady characters.

Eau de Busisiwe

SPRITZ!

PP

Gives you public protection all day long!

GORGONZILLE

When you want to make a stink and cheese people off!

MUESLI MAIMANE

It's not cereal, it's MUESLI - with added bland flavour!

MUESLI MAIMANE

***PRO TEAs* Iced Tea**

PRO TEAs

The energy drink with little or no energy!

ICED TEA

Drink with caution: possible *choking* hazard!

Rama Phosa

The slick & easy spread.

Rama Phosa

Use it every New Dawn!